Early American

EARLY AMERICAN

The Story of Paul Revere

By

MILDRED MASTIN PACE

Illustrated by

HENRY S. GILLETTE

NEW YORK

CHARLES SCRIBNER'S SONS

1941

121

Contents

Illustrations

But now he knew that when a boy turns to a man's trade, he must do a man's work. His day started before it was light. There were fires to build, the shop to open, errands to run, and through the day, long hours at the workbench learning the silversmith's trade.

Paul's father taught him how to melt old pieces of silver and silver coins into shining streams, and how to pour the liquid into even, glistening sheets. He showed him how to hammer the sheets to the needed thicknesses, and the way the silver could be cut to the proper size with shears.

Everything must be done by hand, for there was no machinery, and his tools were few. As his father stood over him, watching and correcting him, Paul learned how to change the silvery sheet into the curved hollow of a bowl. His father showed him how to put handles on with the bright, hot flame of a torch, and how to polish the silver to give it a deep, metallic glow.

Sometimes as they worked, Paul's father would tell him stories, true stories of exciting things that had happened to him. The one Paul loved best to hear and his father loved most to tell, was the story of his coming to America. When Paul was younger, he could scarcely keep from crying when he heard his father tell it. For it was a sad story, even though it had a happy ending.

"I lived with my father and mother in France," the story began, "and when I was a very little boy, I realized that a great, dark shadow hung over our home, and I saw my parents suffering. Sometimes when we walked through the streets, stones and dirt would be thrown at us. Soldiers would stop my father and question him roughly. Men would call him names. When I grew older, I learned that we were persecuted because we were Huguenots and believed differently from others.

"If we spoke what we thought, we faced imprisonment or were sentenced to death. If a knock was heard at our door, we feared the soldiers had come. If a friend was missing at our secret meetings of worship, we knew it was likely that we'd never see him again, and we wondered who would go next. So we lived, always in danger, never free from oppression, with no rights whatsoever in our own land."

And then the older Revere would tell of the dark night when his parents waked him and bade him dress. His mother's face was wet with tears, and his strong, brave father was trembling. They told him he was going to a country where he could grow up doing what he had been taught was right without suffering for it. It was a land of freedom, where men thought, spoke and worshiped as they chose, and no one was persecuted.

He was just twelve years old then, and he was going alone.

Quietly they slipped through the black streets,

down to a waiting boat. And there he told his parents good-bye. The little boat took him to the Isle of Guernsey where an uncle lived, and from Guernsey another, larger boat, carried him across the Atlantic Ocean to Boston.

"I knew no one in Boston," Paul's father went on with the story, "but my uncle had arranged for me to be apprenticed to a goldsmith, so I was shortly busy with work. Then soon I met other Huguenots who had taken refuge here, and I no longer felt I was among strangers. And, though I grieved for my parents, I knew they wanted, more than anything else, to have me safe in America."

Here his father would always pause for a moment before saying, "If you had ever lived under a government of oppression, Paul, you would understand what the freedom here meant, even to a boy. People speaking their minds, with no fear of punishment. People worshiping in peace, without danger of arrest. No soldiers questioning you, no spies tattling. Ah, son, your liberty is a precious thing. Guard it well."

Paul vowed he would! He felt he was fortunate indeed to have been born in a country that was free. He was grateful that he could go with his father and mother and the younger children to the New Brick Chuch on Sunday, and not be afraid. He was thankful that, when he looked out of the window, there were no hostile soldiers passing.

He was glad, too, that his father and not a stranger was teaching him his trade. For as he grew older in his father's service, he became acquainted with other apprentices in Boston—young men learning to be printers and braziers, cutlers, and shipbuilders—and he knew that many of them had a hard time of it.

These apprentices were virtually owned by their masters during the years it took to learn the trade. They worked long, hard hours, and in exchange for their labors received only their keep. They could not buy anything nor sell anything without the consent of their masters; day and night they were under their command, and sworn to obedience.

Paul would hear one complain, "We have scanty fare at my master's table, and the work is heavy." Another would grumble, "There's drudgery enough at our shop to keep three men busy. I could work all night, and it still wouldn't be finished." He heard them swap stories of scoldings and whippings and tell of masters who grew furious at mistakes and angry if the apprentices seemed slow in learning. Paul, hearing these woes, would be thankful for the Revere's cheerful shop and his father's kindly teaching, and he would resolve to show his gratitude by working harder and harder.

One day after Paul had been apprenticed in the shop for several years, his father put a small, sharp tool in his hand and said, "Here is the graver. You

Paul as his father's apprentice

may cut the design on the silver pitcher we have just made."

Paul's dark eyes sparkled, and his hands trembled a little in their eagerness. For this was a kind of final examination, a test of his ability in his father's art.

Paul took the tool and pressed it against the shining metal. His hand must be firm, the marks sure. Beneath his touch the delicate design slowly grew. As his father watched the smooth flow of lines, the careful balance of the pattern, his heart filled with pride. And when the job was finished, he said softly, "Paul, my son, you are not only a good workman, but an artist."

Paul looked down at the pitcher, very happy and yet a little humble at his father's praise. He knew that it was a time of graduation for him, and that from now on important and more creative things would be expected of him.

It was fortunate that Paul was so quick and skillful at the silversmith's trade. He was still an apprentice, and had scarcely grown into manhood, when he realized something was wrong with his father. The older man tired so easily, resting over work he had once rushed through, struggling to lift trays of metal that before he had handled lightly.

As time went on now, more and more of the work fell on Paul's shoulders, for his father's health was failing rapidly. And then, one morning, Paul waked to learn that henceforth he would be alone in the shop.

There was his mother, and younger brothers and sisters for him to care for now that his father was gone. He was nineteen, strong and capable. But he had the full burden of the business, and the work of two men always before him.

Those were long and tedious days for Paul, weary with too much to do. His only consolation was that people admired his work as they had his father's, and customers were pleased with the designs he made. And yet, sometimes, it seemed to Paul that he must spend the rest of his days within the four walls of the shop, that never, as long as he lived, would he ever be able to get away. If any one could have told him of the exciting times just ahead, he would have found it hard to believe.

CHAPTER TWO

Jack of All Trades

PAUL couldn't remember when he had first noticed Sarah Orne. He'd been too busy in the shop to pay much attention to girls. But now, suddenly, he saw that Sarah was different from any other girl in Boston, and he knew he was in love.

Marriage, he realized, would add new responsibilities to a load that was already heavy. But his brothers and sisters were growing up fast, and before many more years they would all be out from under his care.

"Besides," Paul argued with himself, "I'm big and strong; I can handle extra work. And I'm almost tweny-three—it's time I married and started a family of my own."

And so, one hot August afternoon, Paul hurried along North Street toward his home, whistling as he went, gay as a cricket and light of heart, because it was his wedding day, and soon Sarah Orne would be his bride.

By the time another summer came, a baby girl was born to Paul and Sarah. They named her Deborah, and were very proud of her. Before Deborah was two years old, she had a baby brother, Paul Junior. And from then on, for years to come, there was always a baby at the Revere house.

With his family growing rapidly, Paul had to earn more money, and so he began adding other trades to his gold and silver smithing.

He didn't mind hard work, and he considered no honest job beneath him. People had horses that needed shoeing, so Paul became a blacksmith. He made tin whistles and dog collars and handles for carriage whips. He made chains for the boys' pet squirrels and heads for the dandies' canes. His customers would often chuckle over the bills Paul sent out. On one bill there might be charges for a gold locket, the shoeing of a horse, a silver pitcher and a set of sleigh bells!

And, when he learned one day that John Baker, the only dentist in the neighborhood was leaving Boston, he said promptly to himself, "Some one will have to take the man's place—it might as well be you, Paul." So, he decided to add the making of false teeth to his accomplishments. That very night he sat down at his desk and wrote an advertisement to put in the Boston paper:

WHEREAS many Persons are so unfortunate as to lose their Fore-Teeth by accident and otherways, to their great Detriment, not only in Looks, but speaking both in Public and Private:—This is to inform all such, that they may have them replaced with artificial Ones, that looks as well as the Natural & answers the End of Speaking to all intents, by PAUL REVERE, Goldsmith, near the head of Dr. Clarke's wharf, Boston.

All persons who have had false Teeth fixt by Mr. John Baker, Surgeon Dentist, and they have got loose (as they will in time) may have them fastened by the above who learnt the Method of fixing them from Mr. Baker.

In a short time Paul was doing a brisk business in dentistry, numbering Boston's most prominent citizens among his trade. Even George Washington, when he visited Boston and was in need of dental repair, came to Paul for a new set of teeth.

Paul was gradually becoming a Jack-of-all-trades, but each thing he did, he did well. People knew that almost anything they wanted done, Paul could be trusted to do.

One day a young man came into his shop with a roll of canvasses under his arm.

"These are portraits I have painted," he said "and I need proper frames for them. Can you make the frames for me?"

Paul told him he could. The young man unfolded the canvasses, and Paul saw that the portraits were very beautiful. The artist was unknown then, but Paul knew, looking at the pictures, that some day John Singleton Copley would be famous.

Paul enjoyed making frames for John Copley's fine paintings. He would lay gold leaf onto the heavy wood with exquisite care, and work at the carving of the wood until he was sure he had a frame that would enhance the pictures.

Paul and John Copley became friends, although

John Copley painting Paul's portrait

they were very different. Paul was robust; John was inclined to be frail. John dressed as an aristocrat, and looked very handsome in his claret coat with its wide, lace-ruffled cuffs. His hair was kept powdered, and he wore gold knee buckles and fancy buckles on his shoes. Paul wore the simple clothes of a workingman. His hair went unpowdered, and his shoes were stout and practical.

Once when they were together in the shop, John said, "Paul, I would like to paint your portrait. Just as you are, here in the shop."

Paul was surprised, for he knew that John loved to paint the texture of heavy silks and brocades, the frail patterns of fine lace. He said, "I'm no fit subject for your painting, John, unless I put on richer dress."

But the young artist insisted, "No. I want to paint you in your work clothes, as I know you. You should be holding a piece of silver you're working on."

And so he painted the portrait of Revere, the silversmith, in his every-day blue waistcoat and a white shirt, a silver teapot in his hand, his simple tools on a table beside him.

Later, when strife and bitterness separated friends and made enemies of neighbors, Paul often thought of those quiet afternoons at the shop, when John painted while he worked at his silver, and the peace was never broken by argument.

However, even while Paul went calmly along,

building new businesses, proudly watching his little family grow, his life was not as tranquil as it seemed. Things were beginning to happen that planted rebellion in his heart.

In England a new king was on the throne, and his attitude toward the American Colonies was much too highhanded to suit men who cherished their liberty as Paul did.

One of the King's first moves had been to dig up an old law forbidding the Colonies to trade with any country except England. No one had paid much attention to the law before, but now George the Third was determined to enforce it.

This meant that the colonists were no longer free to trade their lumber and fish for the molasses and sugar of the West Indies. Their profitable commerce with the French and the Spaniards must stop.

Perhaps Paul worried because there would now be fewer traders from the Islands bringing golden doubloons and silver coins into Boston. But a shortage of gold and silver was not his chief concern. His great anxiety was that, under the iron hand of the King, the colonists would lose the freedom they prized so highly. British ships of war were already stationed along the New England coast to prevent free trade with the Spanish and French.

Paul saw honest traders become smugglers, for, when the Colonies were not allowed to trade openly with other countries, goods from those lands began to be brought in illegally. On dark nights small boats would slip into the Harbor, laden with forbidden cargoes. During the day, bold brigs flying the British flag, would put in with contraband disguised as English goods. And so, under the cover of darkness and deception, some trade with foreign countries continued.

But it did not take long for the King to hear of this, and now outrageous things began to happen to the people. In order to put an end to the smuggling, the King's officers, armed with pieces of paper called "Writs of Assistance," were permitted to go into anyone's home or shop and search it for contraband goods.

Women had to stand by, indignant but powerless, and watch the officers rummage through their homes, prying into all the cupboards, spying from kitchen to attic. Men watched with mounting anger while the King's officers plundered through their shops. Since an officer could search any place he wished, the searches were often done purely for spite.

Sometimes in the evening, after the day's work was done, Paul and men like him would gather to talk over the plight of the Colonies. Trade had already been crippled so badly that once-prosperous merchants were failing and shipbuilders could no longer stay in business. The King's men were free to force any door, and no home was sure of its privacy. Where would it stop? What would the King do next?

The King's officers searching a home

CHAPTER THREE

At the Green Dragon Inn

It was still early afternoon, but Paul fastened the shutters, locked the door of his shop, and walked toward the Harbor. There was no use trying to do business this day. The people of Boston were too troubled to think of trading, and Paul was too restless for work.

The day was warm with the first of spring. But Paul didn't see the new green of the trees nor the golden sunlight spilled about him. He saw the war vessels in the Harbor, he saw the anxious faces of the men and women and children he passed on the street. And when people spoke to him, their first words were always, "Have you heard?"

Paul would reply, "Yes. Parliament passed the Stamp Act. It will mean trouble." Then, if the person was a man like himself, Paul would add in a low voice, "We are meeting tonight at the Green Dragon Inn."

When Paul returned to his shop later in the afternoon, he closed the door after him, took a smooth sheet of copper down from a shelf, and stood looking at it. Then on a piece of paper he began, rapidly, to sketch.

The Stamp Act had angered him so he had to do something about it at once. Talking was all very well, but Paul Revere was a man of action, and words weren't enough. He would draw a picture that would show the British what one patriot thought of their Stamp Act! He would engrave it on copper, print it by the hundreds, send copies of it everywhere. If there were colonists so slow-witted they wouldn't rebel at the Act, his cartoon would incense them. If there were Englishmen who believed the Act had been docilely accepted by the Americans, they would know differently.

First he drew an ugly dragon, which represented the hated Stamp Act. In front of the dragon stood a man with a drawn sword. He represented Boston, ready to fight. Crowding around were the other Colonies, eager to back Boston up in the battle against the dragon.

As he added details to the sketch, Paul's indignation mounted. In the first place, the King had no right to tax the Colonies. It was a principle of English law that no tax should be levied on the people except by members of Parliament who represented those people. Since the Colonies were not allowed to send anyone to Parliament as their representative, they were being taxed unlawfully.

And, in the second place, the colonists couldn't afford to be taxed. The Stamp Act taxed "every skin or piece of vellum or parchment, or sheet or piece of paper" used in a business or legal way in the Colonies. Paul couldn't buy a newspaper or a calendar or an almanac without having paid, too, for a British stamp. A man couldn't buy a pamphlet or print a simple hand-bill, without paying a stamp tax. A piece of paper telling a man he had been elected to a public office might carry a stamp that cost him as much as four pounds. A college diploma was taxed two pounds. Before a man could survey a piece of land he had to get a warrant and pay the stamp tax. Every bill of lading, a letter relating to the payment of money, a will or deed, had to carry a hated stamp for which the Crown had been paid.

Outside Paul heard a boy shout, "Hey, Lobster!" And then the sound of running feet. He knew that some youngster, perhaps his own son, was taunting a passing British soldier. Even the children resented the sight of the Redcoats.

It was growing dark, and Paul, remembering the important business of the evening ahead, put the half-finished engraving away, and went home for a bite of supper. He would finish the cartoon tomorrow.

When Paul left home that evening, he didn't tell his family where he was going. This was strange, for he was a devoted husband and father and if business did sometimes take him away for an evening, the family always understood why.

But this night Paul took down his hat and his greatcoat, and saying, "It may be very late when I come home, don't wait up for me," he went out into the darkness.

At the Green Dragon Inn, one room was closely shuttered and the heavy curtains drawn so no gleam of light, no sound of a voice, might reach the outside. The men straggled in, that their coming would be less noticeable. Some tarried in the front room of the Inn for a while to divert suspicion, others entered by the back door. Observers might have remarked that the Inn was doing a good business that night, but surely no one would have suspected the truth.

As each man entered the shuttered room, he placed his right hand on a Bible, and swore not to tell anyone of this meeting.

These were serious faces on which the candle light fell. These men, like Paul, were strong and hard working, honest and unafraid. Some of them remembered from their own childhoods in foreign lands the sorrows of living in a country that is not free. Others remembered as Paul did, the sacrifices and hardships their parents or grandparents suffered in order that they might be brought up in America. They had faced separation from those they loved and all the things dear to them. They had faced slow death by starvation and bitter cold, and murder by Indians. Each man at the meeting that night knew that his liberty had been paid for by others' sacrifices. Now a stubborn king three thousand miles away was scheming to crush this freedom that had cost so much.

"But he shall not!" Though Paul was not a great orator, his words rang with courage and sincerity, and every man listened.

There were many things to be decided that night. They would call their organization "Sons of Liberty." Similar groups must be formed secretly in all the other Colonies. At each meeting the men would swear on the Bible that nothing pertaining to that meeting would ever be told. Their society would be so secret they would not even keep a roll of members.

Each man was to be a kind of spy: listening, watching for any information he could get on what the British might plan to do next. Each man was to be ready to fight when the moment came. And, in the meantime, each must do what he could to win people over, one hundred per cent, to the colonists' side. It was very late when the men left the Inn and slipped through the dark streets to their homes.

Paul continued to draw cartoons to stir up feeling against the King. And while the engravings added still another business to his list of trades, they also began to bring Paul a certain amount of fame. Patriotic leaders in nearby towns now asked, "Who is this man that so boldly scoffs at the British? He's a fellow to depend on when a crisis comes!"

As the months went by, more and more patriots

At the Green Dragon Inn

were taken into the Sons of Liberty. It became dangerous for them all to meet together, for a group so large would surely attract attention. They divided, meeting in different parts of Boston.

Sometimes there would be a suspicion that their meeting place had become known. Then a new place for their gatherings would have to be found. Mothers, wives and sisters must have wondered what dark doings were afoot to keep their men out so late at nights. But if they asked, no answers were given, and most of them, knowing of the troubled times, didn't worry the men with questions.

There was a rumor that one woman, a Miss Burroughs, had discovered the Sons' meeting place and hidden in a clothes closet to listen. Apparently what she heard had scared her into silence. At any rate, she never told.

The Sons worked out codes to insure absolute secrecy, and no words regarding their organization ever passed between the men outside meetings. Messages were conveyed by a certain lift of the hand, the nod of a head, arms folded, or the blink of an eye.

The members did wish for some kind of identifying emblem. But to wear a club pin or button for others to see was, of course, out of the question. So Paul made a small silver medal for each member, a medal that could be strung on a fine cord and hung around the man's neck, yet remain hidden beneath his garments.

On each medallion he engraved a strong hand holding high a staff topped with a Liberty Cap, symbol of freedom since the days of Rome.

The Sons of Liberty grew and the people's anger at the Stamp Act grew also. In August, a crowd—some whispered they were Sons of Liberty—made a dummy that looked like the Stamp Collector, hung it from the great elm tree that stood near the Boyleston Market. After that the elm was known as the Liberty Tree, and patriots saluted it as they passed.

As stories such as these reached England, political leaders there became surprised, and some of them were alarmed. Edmund Burke, a member of Parliament, had told them that if the King tried to tax the Colonies without their consent, it would be as difficult as a farmer trying to shear a wolf instead of a sheep. Now there were other Britishers who were willing to agree with Burke.

Finally, when the Sons of Liberty were almost a year old, the King listened to the advice of others and the Stamp Act was repealed.

But if Paul and his friends felt victorious, their rejoicing did not last long. A short while later, word was received that still greater taxes were imposed, that from now on, the Colonists would have to pay Great Britain a duty on all glass, paints, paper and tea!

There was a lot of work ahead for the Sons of Liberty!

CHAPTER FOUR

Soldiers and More Soldiers

CALEB HOPKINS was the fifteenth man who had come into Paul's shop that day—and each of them with silver in his pocket.

Caleb dropped an old spoon and a silver locket on the table, and asked, "Is this enough?"

Paul put the silver on a scale and studied it for a moment. "It's a little more than enough," he said. "Each man's share is three ounces, you know."

"Never mind," Hopkins laughed, "A touch more silver will make the punch bowl that much larger; eh, Paul?"

Outside a July sun poured its scorching heat on streets and houses. Inside the shop it was even hotter, for Paul had a fire going. He wanted to melt the silver. He poured the pieces of silver in a glittering pile, letting them run through his fingers. Silver buckles, silver chains, spoons and rings and silver coins—a little more than forty-five ounces.

Paul had never had a job of silver-smithing that pleased him more. He didn't mind the shimmering waves of heat, the hot flame of the fire. His thoughts, in fact, went back five months to a day in February when all of Boston was excited by a letter that had been written. If it hadn't been for that letter, he wouldn't be standing there now, melting down this silver.

The letter had been drawn up by the Massachusetts Assembly, those men, that is, whom the people of Massachusetts elected to represent them in the state government. Many people, like Paul, were growing more and more resentful of England's attitude toward the Colonies. But they realized, too, that Massachusetts was only one of thirteen Colonies, and that any one Colony all by itself could hardly hope to influence England. However, if all of them could get together and make a united complaint, England might listen.

So the letter was drawn up by the Assembly, one copy of it to go to each Colony, suggesting that they appoint committees to work out plans for some kind of united action to persuade England to right the wrongs in the new land.

The other Colonies received the letter with enthusiasm. But, many weeks later when word of it reached England, the King's government was very angry. An order was sent to Massachusetts demanding that the Assembly rescind, or annul, the letter. The order said that if the Assembly refused to rescind, it should be dissolved and not allowed to meet again until the members apologized.

The ship bringing this order sailed into Boston Harbor on a sunny June day in 1768. It had been just a little more than three years since a similar ship had dropped anchor and brought word that Parliament had passed the Stamp Act. Now, as on that spring afternoon in 1765, excited people with anxious faces filled the streets of Boston, asking each other, "Have you heard the latest news from England?"

On the morning of June the twenty-first the Assembly met. One hundred and nine men, serious, worried.

Outside, the people wondered and guessed and argued. Would the members dare disobey an order from the Government of the King?

"Yes!"

"No!"

"We must take our stand now!"

"England has no right to dissolve our Assembly."

"The members will rescind."

"They won't!"

And while the people in the streets argued and waited for word, the Assembly debated. Day after day the war of words went on, men shouting for rights, men begging for caution. Some believed it was wiser to obey. Others, that obedience meant the end of liberty in America.

For nine days the Assembly wrangled, the people waited.

And when, on the thirtieth of June, the debate ended and a vote was taken, ninety-two members of the Assembly refused to obey the order. Only seventeen agreed to rescind. What heroes those ninety-two men were to the people who believed in the Colonies' cause!

A few days later one of the Sons of Liberty came into Paul's shop and said, "A crowd of us wants to do something to honor the brave ninety-two who refused to rescind. We want a proper memorial, something that in the years to come will remind people that these dared to rebel."

And so, Paul was making the memorial punch bowl. Into it was melted some object of value that had belonged to each of its givers. Made of solid silver, it would not fade with time. It would be a lasting commemoration, and on its smooth sides, Paul would engrave its story.

When the bowl was finished, and stood polished and shining before him, Paul took his engraving tools and began to carve. Round the top of the bowl he engraved the names of the fifteen men whose gift it was. And on one side, its story:

To the Memory of the glorious NINETY Two Members of the Honorable House of REPRESENTATIVES of the MASSACHUSETTS BAY, who undaunted by the Insolent Menaces of Villians in Power, and out of strict regard for Conscience, and the LIBERTIES of their Constituents, on the 30th of June, 1768, VOTED NOT TO RESCIND.

Strong words, those, "the insolent menaces of 'villians' in power." But never mind. Some people needed strong words.

Paul paused in his engraving and looked with satisfaction at a picture on the wall above him. It showed the seventeen rescinders being pushed into the flaming jaws of a dragon by a devil, and beneath was the title, "A Warm Place—Hell." That was Paul's "memorial" for the seventeen who had obeyed the King. And copies of the picture were already all over town, in the hands of delighted patriots.

A caricature for those who were loyal to the King —a silver punch bowl for those who were true to the Colonies!

But there were rumors now that the King, impatient with the Massachusetts Colony's behaviour, was sending whole regiments of troops to Boston.

It was a cool, golden fall day, the last day of September, when the ships laden with soldiers sailed into the Harbor. All of Boston turned out to watch them disembark.

According to the Governor, the soldiers had come "to rescue the government out of the hands of a trained mob." But Paul, and all the other patriots who watched, knew that the soldiers had come to force, if necessary, the will of the Crown on the colonists.

As each soldier stepped onto the wharf he paused long enough to receive sixteen rounds of ammunition. The unarmed citizens, watched and wondered.

The soldiers marched in bright columns, with their scarlet coats and their bayonets shining in the autumn sun. They marched smartly to the rhythm of the fife and drum, and they made a bold and glittering spectacle.

But there were no cheers to greet them, no welcome. The townspeople had only silence and resentment for the King's men.

"Soldiers and more soldiers," Paul said angrily. We are taxed to pay their salaries, taxed to keep them here! A strange kind of freedom we enjoy, with armed Redcoats filling our streets."

After the soldiers were quartered in Boston, the Sons of Liberty became even more vigilant. It was now impossible to keep its existence a secret. While outsiders did not know who its members were, and its meetings and movements were still shrouded in mystery, people knew there was such an organization.

One morning Paul's friend, John Copley, came into the shop. John was not a Son of Liberty. Gentle, peace loving, aristocratic, he hoped that the differences between England and the Colonies could be smoothed out without strife. And he felt that the Sons, by rousing the people, only made a peaceful settlement more difficult. He did not agree with Paul, that the people had to be roused or the cause of the Colonies would be lost. The two friends had spent many hours trying to convince each other.

But this day, John's face was sad, and Paul knew that he had not come to argue.

The soldi

rch into Boston

John said, "Paul, I've come to say good-bye. I've decided to go abroad. There's nothing here but turmoil —I want peace and a chance to paint."

"But, things may be settled here soon, John. Sooner than many people think."

"No, I can't wait for that. There are great artists in Europe from whom I can learn, and, besides, there are fine paintings I want to study."

Paul was sad at the thought of his friend's leaving. But he knew John was right. John was an artist, a genius, not a fighter. With his love of beauty, his aristocratic tastes, the Colonies' cause would disturb him but never inflame him. He would find nothing here, in the years ahead, but grief.

"You may come back later, John?"

"Perhaps."

But, even as Paul watched John walk down the street and out of sight, he knew they would never meet again. Perhaps it was better so, Paul tried to comfort himself with the thought, for they had parted friends. Still, the farewell drove home sharply to Paul the knowledge that the people of Boston were already divided in their sypathies. And that within a few years all men must choose between the Colonies and the land across the sea.

With a heavy heart, Paul turned back to his work.

CHAPTER FIVE

Deborah Takes Charge

THE curtains were drawn at the Revere home, and a great sorrow filled the quiet rooms. The children spoke in whispers, and poor Paul sat in silent despair. For that day his wife, Sarah, had died, leaving their six children in his care.

The youngest, Izanna, was a little baby, not quite five months old. And the oldest, Deborah, was barely fifteen.

A few days later, Paul gathered his family around him, and said, "Children, it is good that you are strong and have courage, for this is a time of great trial for us all. In addition to your grief now, you will be burdened with new responsibilities and much work." Paul's kind eyes turned from one solemn little face to another, and his voice was gentle as he spoke.

"Deborah has been taught well to cook and clean, and she knows how to care for the baby. Sarah's eleven, and old enough to help Deborah with the work. Paul, you're thirteen now, and a stout lad. You must make your sister's work as light as you can. Fetch the wood for her, and keep the water pail filled; carry out the ashes and see to the fires."

Seven year old Frances said, "I can help Deborah, too, Father. There are lots of things I can do."

"I know there are," Paul looked fondly at the children, "and even little Mary here can help by watching the baby."

After that the children had little time to play. From early morning, when Sarah set the pewter porringers on the table while Deborah cooked breakfast, until evening when the last bowl was dried and put away, the children were busy.

Paul always found the house shining clean when he came home in the evening. The wide board floors of the spacious rooms were scrubbed and waxed. The tiny diamond-shaped panes of the leaded windows, so hard to wash, were spotless and gleaming. The furniture was rubbed till it shone.

On washdays, young Paul helped his sister fill the kettles and hang them on the iron crane to be swung over the fireplace for heating. Even Frances could lighten the day's work a little by rubbing the small pieces. By noon the clothes were dancing on the line: the baby's long, white dresses, frocks and breeches and petticoats by the dozen, snowy sheets and ruffled bed curtains, and rag rugs in bright patches between the white things.

As the spring days grew warmer, there were seeds

to be planted in the back-yard gardens, and weeding to be done. Young Paul planted the vegetable patch, corn and beans, squash and pumpkins. Deborah took particular care with the herb garden. There, in neat rows, grew her thyme and rosemary, field balm and mint and basil—all the precious herbs that not only added flavor to her cooking but were concocted into simple home remedies when anybody took sick.

In the back yard, too, the blue-green leaves of the lads-love were showing, and purple violets were starting to bloom. Hearts-ease was budding and the sweet stock grew tall. Deborah was proud of the herbs and flowers. She took time to teach Mary Ann and Frances how to tell the little plants from weeds, and they helped her keep the beds trim and flourishing.

Deborah did all the cooking in the big kitchen fireplace. Over the embers she cooked platters of fish in long-handled, three-legged skillets. From the iron cooking pots that hung on the crane, she poured hot soups and bubbling stews. For special occasions she would put a fat chicken or a fine joint of meat on the spit to roast over the embers.

Once a week was bake day, and that was the workday the children liked best. Very early in the morning young Paul would bring in an armload of hard, dry wood. Beside the fireplace, built into the chimney, was the brick oven. And inside the brick oven, Paul would build a fire. The fire was kept going until the bricks were blistering hot. Then the fire was smothered out, the wood and ashes swept quickly away, and the hot, clean oven was ready for Deborah's foods.

For, while Paul was tending the fire, Deborah was busy. Crocks of beans stood ready for the oven, and besides them, pans of brown bread. Deep pie pans were lined with crust, and the children's eyes danced as they saw Deborah pour sliced apples or blue berries into the waiting shells. There was corn pudding, and a meat pie, and a whole pan full of tarts.

First the beans went in. So deep was the oven, Deborah and young Paul had to push the crocks in with a long-handled peel, or shovel. They put the things in hurriedly, anxious not to waste any of the precious heat.

When the last pie went in, and there was never an inch of oven space left, the iron door was tightly closed. The children could do nothing now but wait until Deborah's nose told her the tarts were done or the meat pie could be taken out. There was never a day when they came to the supper table as hungry as they did on bake day!

But it seemed that there were always more and more jobs to be done. There was preserving to do, and pickles to make, and jelly to be put up. Soon the shorter days of late summer reminded Deborah that in addition to everything else, they must get to candlemaking.

She had carefully saved all the grease she could

Candlemaking in the Revere home

from her cooking. This could be used for "every day" candles. For better candles, they would go into the fields on the edge of town and gather bayberries.

Deborah melted the fragrant wax coating off the bayberries. How many hundreds and hundreds of berries it took to make a single candle! Then the children, carefully holding the wicks, dipped the candles. They knew that the tiniest crook in the wick meant a crooked candle, and each one took pride in dipping candles that were straight and even.

No one grumbled at the many chores. And yet, although young Paul and Sarah and Frances hurried home from school to help until bedtime, Deborah's work seemed never to end.

Paul was proud of his children and the way they managed, but he was worried. The older children had too much to do, and the baby was not well. Deborah kept the baby in a little cradle near her as she worked. Each night the cradle was carried upstairs and set beside her bed. She gave the baby loving care, but Paul could see it growing weaker, instead of stronger, and he knew that Deborah, too, was afraid.

At night, when he left to go to a meeting of the Sons of Liberty, he would stand for a moment looking at the dark house where his children were left alone. Were they safe? Would Deborah hear the baby if it cried?

But he couldn't turn back. The mission before him

was too important. So, he went on, filled with anxieties and doubts.

The baby lived till the end of summer. Every one had known that its hold on life was too frail to last. But to Deborah, especially, the house seemed strange and empty without it, and her heart was heavier as she went about her tasks.

Brave as the children were, they found the work increasingly hard and the home lonely. Their father had to be at his shop all day, and most of the evenings he was away on business they did not understand. Even when he was home, he looked worried and unhappy. Once their house had been full of merry voices and laughter. Now it was quiet, and a stranger passing by would hardly have guessed that children lived there.

Then, one bright October day, Paul came home, bringing them a new mother. She had a quick smile and a light step, and when she walked into the house she brought happiness. Her name was Rachel.

Rachel was young and gentle and loving. In her capable hands, the housework hummed along. There was time in the evenings for them all to sit around the table in front of the big fire, cracking hickory nuts and telling stories. Sometimes Rachel would pour a measure of molasses into a pot and hang it on the crane, and the children would shout with glee because it was a night for candy pulling.

Now Paul, too, could laugh again. Only, he scowled

if any mention was made of the soldiers that filled the town, or of taxes or tea. Especially he scowled at the mention of tea.

When the King's government had taxed the Colonies on glass and paper, paints and tea, following the repeal of the Stamp Act, Paul and many other patriots took an oath promising to buy none of the taxed articles. Patriotic storekeepers refused to sell the taxed merchandise.

The colonists would do without glass, without paint. Of course, it was inconvenient sometimes. Paul, himself, engraved plates for a song book, then couldn't publish it because there was only English-taxed paper to print it on. And the poor preacher of Paul's church, having only a few scraps of paper left, wrote his sermons in such tiny letters he had to use a magnifying glass at services to read them!

Tea from England the patriots did without, too. Even the children knew that when the small store of tea in the Revere cupboard was gone, they would do without, or use tea smuggled from Holland.

Soon, of course, the English government saw the folly of taxing things that people would not buy and in ruining trade by keeping the colonists angry. So all the taxes were repealed, finally, except the one on tea.

The tea tax was not a large tax. In fact, it was so small that the amount it yielded the British government was unimportant. The tax was kept on, not for the money, but to show the Colonies that the British government felt it had a right to tax them.

Paul thundered, "It's as vicious as if all the taxes were left on! We are still being taxed, unfairly, by a government in which we have no voice."

The colonists could buy the taxed tea from England cheaper now than the smuggled tea from Holland. But if even the tiniest tax was imposed upon it, they swore they wouldn't take the British tea as a gift!

The British government did not believe this. Englishmen said, "The Colonists are only bluffing. We have taken enough of their nonsense. They are acting like spoiled children, and England must treat them as such."

So ships with cargoes of tea set sail for the Colonies. And three of them were headed for Boston.

On a blustery fall night, when the wind was carrying the tea ships steadily toward Boston Harbor, the Sons of Liberty held a special meeting. Each man raised his right hand, and in a firm voice made the solemn oath: "I promise to oppose, with my fortune and my life if necessary, the selling of the tea."

CHAPTER SIX

The Boston Tea Party

ONE day the children saw Rachel making a strange garment. She was sewing bright feathers on dark cloth, and when they asked her what it was, she shook her head and put the sewing away.

At suppertime that evening she brewed a great pot of tea, and poured a little for each child, saying, "Children, this is the last cup of tea you will get for a long while." There was no laughter in Rachel's usually merry voice, and the children drank the tea in silence.

Long after they were asleep that night, Rachel sat sewing on the feathered garment, listening anxiously for the sound of Paul's hand on the latch.

In the dark harbor were the three tea ships, huddled close together at the same wharf. Along the wharf, and above the whistle of the December wind, could be heard the poundings of a sentry's footsteps. A man came out of the darkness and went up to the sentry.

"Paul," he said, "It's half after midnight. You go home and rest, and I'll take your post."

It was a cold night, with ice in the wind, and late

enough so that Boston should have been sleeping. But as Paul walked on toward home, he noticed that there were lighted rooms in some of the houses. And along the dark streets he paused several times to speak to passers-by he knew. For now the Sons of Liberty were keeping twenty-four hour vigils, and many of them were up and about in spite of the hour.

Some of them patrolled the streets, watching for any gathering of soldiers or suspicious activity. There were rumors that the Governor had been advised to mass the regiments of troops and force the landing of the tea. If any such move were made, the Sons were determined to be the first to know of it.

Others of the Sons patrolled the wharf or stood on the dark decks of the ships, muskets in hand, ready to fight if unloading the tea was attempted. The whole town was boiling with excitement.

The excitement had started several days earlier, on Sunday, November 28th, 1773, when the *Dartmouth* sailed into Boston Harbor with one hundred and fourteen chests of tea.

Early the next morning, crowds were gathered to read a summons that had been posted. Nobody knew who had printed it. Nobody knew who had posted it. But it was written in bold language, and no one could mistake its meaning.

Friends! brethren! countrymen!—
That worst of plagues, the detested tea, shipped for this

port by the East India Company, is now arrived in this
harbour,—the hour of destruction or manly opposition to
the machinations of tyranny stare you in the face. Every
friend to his country, to himself, and posterity, is now
called upon to meet at Faneuil Hall, at nine o'clock
this day, at which time the bells will ring, to make an
united and successful resistance to this last, worst, and
most destructive measure of administration.

It was a strange Monday morning in Boston. Men
stood in anxious little groups on the streets, waiting for
the bells to ring. Women sat indoors, their bonnets on,
the children in their best clothes beside them, and listened for the signal.

Crowds of people poured through the streets toward
the meeting place at the ringing of the bells. Faneuil
Hall could never hold so many! Men shouldered their
way through the throngs, calling out, "Turn back to
the Old South Meeting-house—there are too many of
us for the Hall."

More than five thousand strong, they packed into
the building and waited for Samuel Adams' booming
voice to call the meeting to order.

Sam Adams, like Paul, was a leader of the patriots.
And, like Paul, he was clamoring for action. The
sending of the tea ships was an insult that the colonists dared not take meekly. They must act, and act
boldly.

Sam Adams' speech was a tempest, and his words
were words of fury. He kindled fire in the eyes of those

who listened and put rage in their hearts. The crowd's cheers punctuated his sentences, and when he finished, Old South quaked with applause.

There were speeches and more speeches, men rising from the floor to voice their opinions, the people clapping or hissing satisfaction or dissent.

At noon the meeting adjourned long enough for the people to eat. But when a whole town is bursting with words and whipped into a frenzy of excitement, there is little time for hunger. So early afternoon found the crowd crushing back into the meetinghouse, and cries for speeches were begun anew.

By sundown a vote had been taken, and it was resolved that the tea must go back to England in the ship that had brought it. Then, in order to make sure that not so much as a pinch of the tea was removed from the ship, twenty-five men were chosen, among them, Paul, to guard it. They weren't taking any chances with that tea, those Sons of Liberty. They even deposed the master of the ship and made one of their own men captain. Now the Sons were in complete charge of the hated cargo.

A few days later the other two ships, with their cargoes of tea, sailed into the harbor, and the guard had to be increased. It was no easy job the Sons of Liberty had taken upon themselves. Through the bitter cold days and the long nights they watched, going without sleep, neglecting their business, and facing, always, the possibility of an unequal battle if the troops were called out.

As Paul stood guard on the dark wharf, his clothes frosted with salt spray and the wind tearing at him, he must have thought longingly of his snug little house where Rachel waited and the children slept.

Only one thing was certain: the tension couldn't last more than twenty days in all. For there was a law that within twenty days after a ship docked, its cargo must be unloaded and entered at the custom-house, and the tax on the goods paid. If, after twenty days, this had not been done, the customs authorities must seize the cargo and sell it at auction to the highest bidder.

The owner of the *Dartmouth*, a man named Rotch, was quite willing to take his ship, tea and all, and sail it back to England. But there was a law that no ship could leave the harbor unless it had clearance papers. And the royal government flatly refused Rotch clearance papers until the tea was unloaded, the tax paid.

December the seventeenth was the dead line. What would happen then? Perhaps the governor, frightened, would issue clearance papers at the last moment. If not, the colonists must act or be accused of bluffing. As day followed day, and the three ships stayed anchored in the harbor, the flaming excitement in the town was fanned to white heat.

In spite of a sharp wind and the snow underfoot, the morning of December sixteenth found the roads leading into Boston busy with travelers. Walking and a-horseback, in carriages and carts and farm wagons, they poured into the city from Roxbury and Dorchester, Cambridge, Sudbury, and all the neighboring towns. People knew for miles around that at the great mass meeting that day the fate of the tea ships would have to be decided.

In Boston, though it was a weekday, shops were closed, schoolchildren ran through the streets. The tall masts bundled together at Griffin's wharf told the people that the ships had not moved.

Even Old South couldn't hold the mobs of people that day. They jammed it to the walls, and still spilled out into Marlborough and Milk Streets. And while orations thundered inside the meetinghouse, soap-box speakers outside poured words of burning patriotism into the ears of the freezing throngs.

The crowds grew with the day. By mid-afternoon every one was certain that the royal governor did not intend to solve the matter peaceably by issuing clearance papers.

Then through the packed hall and the mobbed streets ran the word that Rotch himself was going to the governor to plead for the papers. Of all the frenzied people in that great crowd, none was more frantic than poor Rotch, whose ship with its cargo was at stake. Even a patriot as staunch as Paul felt sorry for the tea-ship owner.

It was growing late in the afternoon when Rotch set out for the town of Milton, where the governor was staying. At the meetinghouse, the people waited. Darkness fell, and candles were lighted. The rousing speeches continued and patriotic fervor rose with every word.

But why had Paul Revere and a number of his friends suddenly left the meeting? Nobody answered the whispered question.

It was well after dark when Rotch, exhausted and half-frozen, stumbled into the meetinghouse. As he walked up the aisle to meet Samuel Adams a great hush fell over the crowded room. Rotch shook his head, and a sentence told his story. The governor had refused.

Thousands of eyes turned now to Samuel Adams. What were they to do? There was a long minute of suspense, then Adams' voice broke the silence.

"This meeting can do nothing more to save the country!"

The words were hardly spoken when the hall shook with the bellowing of an Indian war whoop. From nowhere had come fifty Mohawks, gaudy with war paint and bright feathers, brandishing tomahawks. Their blood-curdling cry was taken up by crowds in the hall. And as they sped, leaping and yelling, into the moonlit night, the people followed. Straight to Griffin's wharf they ran.

On the way to the Boston Tea Party

The men on guard there stepped aside and let the Indians pass. They swarmed onto the three tea ships; their painted figures eerie in the pale light of the moon. But now there were no war whoops, no wasted motions. These were not yelling Indians, but serious men with a job to be done.

Quietly, efficiently, the chests of tea were brought up, split open, and dumped into the sea. For more than two hours the work went on, and the crowd on the wharf watched in awed silence. There was no sound but the smash of hatchets on chests and the splash of tea as it hit the water. Eighteen thousand pounds of tea were poured into Boston Harbor that night.

When the job was finished, the men tidied up the decks and put everything in order. The ships were exactly as they had been before, except that the tea was gone.

The Indians then seemed to melt away into the night, disappearing as mysteriously as they had come. But those who watched could pretty well guess the identity of the men, and the Revere children knew, now, why Rachel had sewn bright feathers on dark cloth.

The shivering mob on the wharf began to move, breaking into small groups, heading for their homes. These were silent, thoughtful people, with no heart this night for merrymaking. They felt no victory in the destroying of the tea. They knew it was the colony's first bold stroke against the mother country. And they knew it was serious.

Paul walked home slowly, cold and tired. Guarding the tea, he had had no sleep for the past two nights, and the day just ended had been long and strenuous. Tell-tale traces of war paint still stained his face. The blanket he had worn, Indian fashion, he now carried under his arm.

Candlelight glowed in the windows of the Revere house, and Paul felt comforted at the thought of the warm kitchen with food on the fire, and Rachel waiting.

Rachel had just ladled up a steaming bowl of chowder for him when there was a knock at the door. Three men, friends of his and Sons of Liberty, stepped in out of the cold night.

"Paul," one of the men spoke. "The Committee of Correspondence has chosen you to carry the true story of the destruction of the tea to New York and Philadelphia. Can you leave before dawn?"

CHAPTER SEVEN

Paul Revere, Courier

RACHEL brought Paul's greatcoat from the unheated bedroom and spread it in front of the kitchen fire to warm. She looked at the small stack of clean clothes on the table, and checked over them again to make sure nothing had been forgotten. The house was quiet, except for Rachel's light movements and the scratching of a quill pen on paper.

Paul stopped writing, and held the paper to the fire to dry the ink, then he handed it to Rachel.

"Tell young Paul to attend to everything as I've written it," he said. "It's a bad time to leave the shop, just before Christmas. But there's no help for it. Remind him he's the man of the house now, and responsible, while I'm gone."

Outside, the wind threw a handful of sleet against the pane, and a horse pawed the frozen ground impatiently. Rachel shivered and fear darkened her eyes.

"New York seems so far. . . ."

Paul took her in his arms. "It just sounds far," he comforted her. "I'll be back before you know I'm gone."

Rachel smiled at his lie. One minute she was proud

of his being chosen for the journey, the next fearful of his going.

"You'll be gone over Christmas, Paul."

"Yes, I know. I thought of that," he said gently. "We'll have another Christmas when I get back."

She lifted up the greatcoat for him, handed him the carefully packed saddlebag and his pistols. She watched, at the open door, until he was out of sight in the darkness, and listened until the wind blew away the sound of the horse's hoof-beats. His going was hard for both of them.

Paul hurried his horse a little. He would like to make Watertown before daylight. Ten miles to Watertown. He must be careful not to tire his horse. She was fleet and sure-footed, and a good horse was important to him. But speed was important too.

For, if the British, or loyalists, carried the news first, they might tell a false story. They might even convince people in the other colonies that the Boston men were an outrageous bunch of ruffians who had destroyed the tea for the sport of it. Such a story, if believed, would poison popular opinion.

Besides, there were probably tea ships by now in New York harbor and the port of Philadelphia. If patriots there knew in time that Boston had rebelled, they too would have the courage to refuse the tea.

The first light of dawn was behind him, and darkness still ahead, when Paul clattered into Watertown. He stopped at a tavern to drink a bowl of hot milk and to give his horse a short rest, then pressed on toward Sudbury. Paul had never before been far out of Boston. These were strange roads to him, and he did not know what lay beyond the low hills.

At night it seemed queer to stop at an inn and be treated as a stranger. Paul was not used to being a stranger. He had always been among people he knew. His directions were to go directly to the home of John Lamb, Sons of Liberty leader, on reaching New York.

If I ever get there, Paul thought grimly. For the roads were rutty now, and he had to do most of his riding during daylight hours when he and the horse could see the treacherous holes. There were icy stretches too, where Paul got down and led the horse, both of them slipping and sliding and picking their way.

Still, the miles clicked off and towns were left behind—Shrewsbury, Worcester, Brookfield, Kingston.

Wherever he stopped, for warmth or food or sleep, whether it was tavern or farmhouse, some one gave him advice on the road ahead.

"The bridge is out near Enfield and the ice not thick enough to hold you. You'll have to ford the stream. Water's mighty cold."

"Watch the hill just beyond Durham. It's a bad one in the winter."

"Good thing you're a-horseback instead of on

wheels. Roads are so full of holes since the fall floods, wheels can't stand up. Take it slowly between Milford and Fairfield or you'll break a leg."

The advice came in exchange for Boston news that Paul brought. He never stopped but what some one asked, "How are things in the big town?"

Then Paul would tell the story of the Tea Party. And voices would be raised in agreement or heads would shake with disapproval. Paul left a trail of excited talk behind him.

On the fifth day of his journey, just at dusk, Paul sighted New York. A moment before, he had been numb with the cold, and so tired he could scarcely stay on his horse. But now he was warmed with the excitement of what lay before him, and he forgot his weariness.

Lights were coming on in the town, smoke rose from a thousand chimneys. Beyond the houses and the chimneys was the harbor, bristling with the masts of ships. It was bigger than Boston, Paul thought.

He spurred his horse, faster. He was off the bumpy road, onto a street lined with buildings. In spite of his hurry and exhilaration, his eyes missed nothing, and all that he saw he remembered.

The streets, he noticed, were grander than Boston's. They were covered with pebble, and many of them sloped toward the center, making a kind of gutter that, Paul remarked to himself, would be practical in rainy weather. There were more brick houses here, too, than in Boston. In Boston most of the buildings were frame. Paul considered the dark red bricks very handsome.

He was watching carefully for landmarks, now, and following the directions given him for reaching John Lamb's house. There was the square of park with the King's statue in the center. That would be Bowling Green. A church, a school, a tavern, go left, right, turn north.

It was dark when he reached the house. His hands were so stiff with cold, he could scarcely lift the iron door knocker.

The door opened to him, and a man stood there, lamp in hand. He was a big man, and Paul could see in the lamplight that he had a strong, handsome face.

"Are you John Lamb?" Paul asked.

"I am, sir."

"I'm Paul Revere. I have a message for you."

"Revere! From Boston?" Lamb's voice was incredulous. "Come in. By Jove! Come in! How did you get here?"

"Horseback, and I just rode in. My poor animal is at your hitching post."

The house was filled with John Lamb's shouting. His voice was full and vibrant, and Paul, listening to him giving simple orders, knew why Lamb was famous for his speeches.

"Bring something hot for the man to drink—he's frozen. More wood for the fire, Willie. See to the horse, some one. Get those saddlebags in."

There in front of the fire, Paul handed John Lamb the letter from the Committee of Correspondence. John read it half-aloud:

The bearer is chosen by the Committee from a number of gentlemen who volunteered to carry you this intelligence. We are in perfect jubilee. . . . The spirit of the people throughout this country is to be described by no terms in my power. Their conduct last night surprised the admiral and the English gentlemen, who observed that these were not a mob of disorderly rabble (as had been reported) but men of sense, coolness and intrepidity.

Then Paul told the whole story of the Tea Party. When he had finished, John Lamb said, "It was a bold stroke. But magnificent. What an example you fellows set for the rest of us!"

"There are tea ships here?" Paul asked.

"Yes."

"What does your governor propose to do about them?"

"I don't know. But he must hear of this. The Sons are meeting within an hour. What news you have for them!"

Paul said thoughtfully, "Do you have a man who can ride on to Philadelphia?"

"Yes," Lamb answered, "I'll send a man off at

once. Now you must have some supper. And I'll be back for you in time for the meeting."

It was a night of victory for Paul. John Lamb's men were jubilant at the message he brought, and Paul was their hero. Again and again they asked him to repeat parts of the story, to tell them more details, until he was hoarse from talking and his ears ached with their cheers. By midnight there was cause for further celebration. New York's Governor Tryon sent word that the tea ships would be returned to England, their cargo intact. No need for spilled tea in New York harbor!

Back at Lamb's house that night, Paul said, "It's kind of you to want me to stay. But I must leave in the morning. There are men in Boston waiting anxiously for the news I bring. And, too, I want to get back to my family."

John was disappointed. But Paul's horse was ready at dawn.

And when he and John Lamb said good-bye, each man knew that he had made a friend. Neither realized how soon Paul would be back with another and more serious message.

Paul spent Christmas Day on the frozen roads, urging his tired horse on, hoping to reach the tavern at Springfield where he could get a holiday dinner by nightfall. He was still almost a hundred miles from home. Two more days of hard riding!

It was after dark when Paul rode into Boston and

hurried his horse up North Street toward home. Through the window, Paul could see Rachel and the children in the firelit kitchen. He flung open the door, laughing at their surprise. They hadn't dared to hope for his return so soon. Eleven days he'd been gone, but five hundred miles is a long way over winter roads.

A minute later the kitchen was filled with a babble of happy voices. Deborah swung the crane over the fire to heat some food for her father. Everybody was full of questions, but Paul silenced the children good-naturedly.

"I'll tell you all about New York tomorrow," he said. "Right now I'm hungry as a wolf, and must eat. After that I'll have to leave for a little while and deliver a message."

The eager children looked crestfallen. But Rachel said, "It's enough that we're all here together again, safe and happy. There'll be plenty of time for talk."

Young Paul turned to go out and see after the horse, then, as if he hated to speak of it, he said slowly, "Mr. Bentley came by the shop this evening, Father. He wondered when you were getting back. Seems they've been keeping a guard of twenty five to thirty men around the tea ships to make sure no damage is done them, and your name was drawn for tonight's watch."

Rachel looked quickly at Paul, her eyes worried.

Paul said, "Run over to Bentley's, son, and tell him

I'll be at the wharf before midnight. There are some men I must see first."

Before he left the house, he told Rachel of the good news he brought Boston.

"Oh, Paul, I'm so glad. And so proud of you." She tried bravely to keep the note of anxiety out of her voice. "Are you very tired?"

"Tired? Of course not. After all, I've been sitting down most of the time for eleven days." He laughed, and kissed her, and was gone.

Paul stood at his post, stomping his feet for warmth, and watched a gray dawn slowly spread its light. Suddenly the early quiet was broken by the sound of a church bell ringing. Another bell started up, then another and another—until a great chorus of bells chimed over Boston.

Paul, stood on the wharf and listened, knowing they were ringing because he had returned with good news. Soon the whole town was wakened. Nightcapped heads were thrust out open windows, doors left ajar while people asked, "What is it? What's happened?"

And men on the street shouted the joyful answer, "Revere is back. New York joins Boston in forbidding tea to land. We are not alone."

CHAPTER EIGHT

Hard Times in Boston

EVEN as he listened to the jubilant ringing of the bells, Paul wondered just what the King would do to punish Boston for the blow she had struck. It would take six weeks for the news to reach England. Then, Paul figured, there would be weeks of outraged speeches, consternation, debate in Parliament. It would be spring before the waiting colonists would know what form the King's anger had taken.

When it came, no one in all Boston was prepared for the violence and unfairness of it.

The town heard the news early one May morning. As punishment, Boston port was to be closed to all trade until the town paid for the destroyed cargoes and agreed to import taxed tea.

The people were stunned. Close the port of Boston? It was impossible! Why, Boston harbor held as many as five hundred ships. The necessities of life came by boat. Most of the trade depended on the sea. The people would starve, the town would die, there would be no work, no business, nothing for the men to do, nothing for the children to eat.

But Parliament had passed the law. Patrol boats

were there, ready to encircle the harbor and make sure no ship moved.

Furthermore, the peace-time governor was to return to England, and a military governor was coming to take his place. General Gage and four regiments of troops were on their way to rule Massachusetts!

Boston, alone, could not cope with the disaster. Now, as never before, she needed the help of her sister colonies. New York could probably be counted on. Philadelphia, with its important port, its powerful merchants, could it be enlisted too? From there the cry for aid would spread to the south, but first some one must go, as fast as a horse could carry him, to Philadelphia.

Again Rachel packed Paul's saddlebag, and watched him ride off before daybreak.

The air was sweet with the dampness of spring, and fruit trees blossomed along the roadsides. Daylight came earlier now and stayed longer. Oh, it was a different ride from that other one, in more ways than one.

This time Paul rode with no feeling of jubilation, but a sense of despair, and the news he carried called forth no cheers. In each town he paused just long enough to tell the people what had happened and to ask their help.

He carried the message to John Lamb in New York, but he did not tarry. Six days after leaving Boston, he tore into Philadelphia, having ridden three hundred and fifty-six miles in all.

That night in Philadelphia, a great mass meeting was held. Paul sat there, tired and travel-stained, listening to the moneyed merchants, who feared for their trade, advise caution. He heard patriots like himself argue that what had happened in Massachusetts could happen in Philadelphia, and that they would all be lost unless they stood together.

Far into the night they wrangled and argued, and Paul waited tensely for their decision. When it came, the patriots had won. Paul carried a message back to Boston so radical that even the most ardent Son of Liberty had scarcely dared hope for it.

Not only would Philadelphia aid Boston. But she proposed that the colonies organize a central government of their own, to meet in Philadelphia—a governing body with representatives from each state, to decide on what actions the colonies as a whole should take.

And so, shortly after Paul returned to Boston with this momentous proposal, he saw dear old Sam Adams, and four other men start out for Philadelphia: Massachusetts' first delegates to the Continental Congress. The government, actually, had been taken out of the hands of the King!

But now, in Boston, began a time of desperate need. Empty ships rocked and rotted in the harbor. Vessels laden with needed goods approached the port and were turned back by the King's boats. Shops were closed because there was nothing to sell and little money with which to buy. Men who had always worked wandered along the streets and the wharfs. Those who were fishermen stared at the fishing boats they couldn't sail. Whaling ships, and those who manned them, sat idle while Boston ran low on oil. Builders had no work, because there was no way of getting timber and lime and bricks into Boston. Offices closed; traders, sail-makers, caulkers, peddlers, all were shut off from the making of a living.

At first the people took heart a little because it was understood that coastwise ships from neighboring colonies, carrying fuel and food, would be allowed to enter the harbor. But they learned, very shortly, that it was folly to hope for help by sea.

For the small, inadequate harbor at Marblehead had been made the official port, now that Boston was closed. And before a ship carrying needed supplies could land at Boston, it had to first put in at the crowded port of Marblehead for inspection. There the custom officers, in the service of the King, maliciously required all the food or wood to be taken out of the ship, examined, and re-loaded. This might take days, during which time food spoiled and cargoes were pilfered.

Furthermore, if the ship were lucky enough to pass inspection and finally reach Boston's idle harbor, it could not leave Boston until the owner or an agent in the owner's behalf, traveled more than forty miles to Plymouth and received clearance papers from the custom-house there.

Thus the long delays, ruined cargoes, the tedious overland trip to Plymouth made shipping to Boston so uncertain and expensive that even the most altruistic boat owner dared not risk carrying goods to the impoverished and starving city.

The other colonies were helping as much as they could. Along the roads leading into Boston came cartloads of farm produce, great cans of milk, tubs of butter, baskets of eggs. Wagons came rolling in: from the grainfields of the south, from the fertile farms of Pennsylvania and the Jerseys and New York. Flocks of geese, herds of sheep and cattle, were driven in by tired farmers who had walked many miles with their awkward charges.

But it wasn't enough. Roads were rough, travel by wagon slow and expensive. Boston had always been supplied by boats.

Food grew scarce, the necessities of life were giving out, one by one.

Rachel would put a pot of garden greens on the fire and say, "It's a good thing this happened in the summer time. But for the farms and our gardens, we'd all starve."

Soon, however, the days grew shorter; and the

people knew that before long a frost would kill the gardens, and winter would make the roads more and more difficult for wagons to get through.

When the first hint of frost touched the air, early in September, a quiet group of men met at a house in the little town of Milton. There were tradesmen from Boston, farmers from the near-by countryside, storekeepers from the villages. Every town and hamlet in Suffolk County was represented. They were a calm but desperate group, determined to take steps so strong the King could not ignore their plight nor their purpose.

Before the afternoon was over, they had drawn up a set of resolutions, known as the Suffolk Resolves, that severed them forever from the mother country.

The King's conduct, they declared, justified their breaking their allegiance to him. From now on, no money was to be paid by the tax collectors to the governor's treasury. Each hamlet was advised to elect its own military officers. And in order to enforce the Resolves, they said that if any colonist were arrested by the Crown's soldiers for political reasons, the colonists in turn would seize an officer from the King's army.

The only sound in the room was Joseph Warren's voice reading the final draft of the Resolves. Paul stood by the door, listening, his dark eyes glowing, his mouth set in a grim, determined line. The other men, too, weighed each word as Warren spoke it.

When he finished, the Resolves were unanimously accepted as they stood. No move was made to soften them, no motion to make them less defiant.

These Suffolk men represented only a very small part of the thirteen colonies. What they had just done was treason. Any one of them, all of them, could hang for it. But in revolting against the King, they had been driven by desperate need. As his subjects, they had taken more than they could stand. Would the other colonies, and the rest of Massachusetts, back them up?

Eyes turned to Paul. He was now their official messenger. If the Resolves could be taken to Philadelphia, where the Continental Congress sat, delegates from Massachusetts might influence the representatives of the other colonies to endorse them.

For the third time in less than a year, Paul set out from Boston. When he returned, thirteen days later, the bells again rang out at the news he brought.

For the other colonies had not been frightened by the boldness of the Resolves. They approved them, and agreed to support them. If necessary, they would *fight* to right the wrong that had been done Massachusetts!

Even while Boston rejoiced at this spirit of union, the shadow of hunger deepened over the city.

Now the women counted anxiously the number of filled jars remaining on the storeroom shelves, the amount of dried corn left in the bins. Children were content with a supper of boiled mush, and if there was a little molasses left for sweetening, they were very lucky.

In the Revere household, in spite of the troubled times, there was a special reason for happiness. Shortly before Christmas a new baby brother was born. He was Rachel's first child, and they named him Joshua.

Rachel, though happy with her child, was worried about Paul. She saw him mysteriously busy with things he could not talk about—and she knew what he did was dangerous.

For the patriots of Boston—though their jobs had been taken from them, their businesses forced to close —were not idle. They were busy practising disguises, working out codes. They slipped through the darkness at night, lurked in the shadows by day, listening, watching, and Paul, long a spy in the service of the Sons, was their leader and trainer.

No soldier moved that a pair of eyes did not follow. If a Redcoat whispered, somebody heard. The governor's every step was known before he acted. Important papers were intercepted, official messages repeated.

The King's men were baffled. How could the colonists anticipate every move they made?

In addition to the espionage, the patriots were busy collecting pistols and muskets, powder and shot, into precious little stores. When the time came, they would be ready. Gunpowder was scarce, weapons few, because

The patriots storing munitions

the colonists were not permitted to import munitions. But all they could lay their hands on, any each man could spare, were gathered together and hidden carefully in places the British might not suspect.

So the winter passed, with Boston hungry and shabby, but uncomplaining. Her women were worried, her men were now spies and rebels.

In mid-April, one Sunday afternoon, Paul climbed on a horse and turned the animal toward Lexington. Above all else, he was thankful the sun was shining. Had it been a rainy day, his plan of action might have been impossible. Men seldom rode for pleasure in the rain.

He rode in a leisurely manner. He stopped to greet friends, took time to notice the puddley fields, the budding trees.

No one—not even a British soldier—would suspect him of being a spy, on his way with a message of burning importance. He rode along, unhurried so he would not attact attention, walking his horse like any man out only to enjoy an early spring day.

In Lexington he went direct to the house of the Reverend Jonas Clark, where the two patriotic leaders, John Hancock and Sam Adams, were staying. There he told them what he and his men had learned: the British had moved their transport boats close to the warships. They had checked the boats for repairs, made them ready for immediate use. Movements of troops, furthermore, indicated there would soon be action. And it was suspected that the British planned to seize the munitions and supplies the colonists had hidden at Concord. Paul believed, too, that on their way to Concord they meant to stop at Lexington and take both Adams and Hancock as traitors.

"Nothing more is known now," Paul finished, "but you will be warned as soon as the Redcoats move."

Paul left then, starting back slowly for Boston. He must still keep up the disguise of leisure. He made one stop, in Charlestown, just long enough to arrange with a man about some signal lanterns.

It was long after sundown when Paul reached home. Twenty miles away, in Concord, farmers were already hauling muskets and cannon, balls and powder to secret places. In farm wagons, hidden beneath straw, in carts buried under potatoes and grain sacks, the stores of Concord were safely scattered to Bedford and Groton, Lancaster, Acton and other near-by towns. The British would find nothing in Concord but disappointment, thanks to Paul Revere.

Back in Boston, Paul ate a hurried meal, then went out into the night. Vigilance must be doubled. The smallest move of the British now must not be missed.

All night Sunday, Monday and Monday night, all day Tuesday, Paul and his men watched and waited.

CHAPTER NINE

A Light in the Tower

TUESDAY night brought a whisper of activity on Boston Common. The moon was rising, and in the pale wash of light, Paul could see soldiers quietly gathering, marching down toward boats that waited at the water's edge. The British were on the move at last, and they were going by sea.

Paul sped home. He wasn't surprised to find a man waiting with the message, "Joseph Warren wants to see you, and in great haste." For Warren, Paul's friend and leader of the Sons, had been chosen to decide when the alarm should be spread to Lexington and Concord, and to dispatch the messengers.

Warren was sending another Son of Liberty, William Dawes, to Lexington by land. But if Boston Neck, which Dawes had to cross, were guarded, the man might never get through.

So Warren asked Paul to take the hazardous water route: across the Charles River by boat, then on by horseback. This was desperately dangerous, because it was against the law to cross the Charles River after nine o'clock at night and British war vessels lay in wait there to halt or fire upon any boat that dared try it.

Paul was prepared for this emergency. He had a small boat hidden on the bank of the river for just such an errand.

At home he paused long enough to put on boots and a dark coat. There was a hurried good-bye with Rachel. Neither of them dreamed how long the separation was to be, nor the anxiety each would suffer before they met again.

As Paul left the house, his faithful dog followed. Paul stopped to turn him back, but the dog thrust his nose trustingly into his master's hand, and Paul decided his company would do no harm. In fact, a man with his pet beside him might arouse less suspicion than a man walking the dark streets alone. Guards were already out, and it was no time to risk being questioned by soldiers.

Paul made one stop on his way to the river. He had to see Robert Newman, sexton of the North Church, before leaving Boston.

It was a dangerous pause, for troops were quartered in the sexton's house. On this night, at this hour, the faintest movement was viewed with suspicion. Paul's visit there not only endangered himself, but imperiled Robert Newman and his family.

The house was dark. Paul had to rap and call Newman's name to rouse the sexton. They stood in the dim entry way, praying that no soldier had been wakeful, and Paul whispered the order. Two lanterns must be hung at once in the tower of the church. Yes, he knew it was dangerous, especially if a suspecting soldier had been disturbed. But on the shore at Charlestown men had watched since Sunday night for a signal. The two lanterns would tell them that the enemy was leaving Boston, coming by sea. Then, if Dawes and Revere were both halted by the British, the watchers at Charlestown could ride on with the alarm.

Near the river, Paul was joined by two friends who had offered to risk rowing him across.

Together they pulled the hidden boat from its shelter. One of the men slipped an oar into place. The oar screeched in the oarlock, and the three men froze into silence. Something must be found to muffle the oars! They'd have the whole British fleet after them if they tried to cross the river with a noise like that!

Paul motioned them to tie up the boat again. He crept to the nearest house. Just as he reached it, the candle that had spread a faint gleam in an upstairs room was snuffed out. But the window was open, and Paul called softly the name of the woman who lived there. She was loyal to the colonists, he knew.

Speaking in little more than a whisper, Paul told her of their plight. No one came to the window, no voice answered. But in a moment a flannel petticoat

Paul and his friends prepare to cross the river

was tossed from the dark room, into Paul's arms. It was still warm, and Paul smiled, knowing the wearer had hurried with her undressing to donate a garment for a good cause.

Now, surely, he could be off. But as they ripped the skirt into the needed strips, Paul's heart dropped suddenly. After all his careful preparations, he had, in his hurried leave-taking, forgotten his spurs!

He would be riding a strange horse. The need for speed and prompt obedience to his commands would be essential. He must have the spurs. Yet, to go back was unthinkable. There would be more soldiers out by now, stronger guards posted around Boston. He had been lucky to get through before. To risk it again was folly. If one of the others was sent, soldiers spotting a man going into the house of Paul Revere at this time and hour would be suspicious. The man would be followed. They might all three be taken here at the boat.

Then Paul looked down and saw his dog. The dog turned expectantly toward his master, his tail wagging, his ears cocked. The dog, too, seemed to realize there was a great need for silence. He had been so quiet Paul had forgotten till that moment that he hadn't gone back.

Now Paul took a small lead plummet from his pocket and a slip of paper. He wrote "spurs" on the paper, and tied it securely to the dog's collar.

It was less than half a mile back to the Revere

house. The animal could make it faster than a man, and who would be suspicious of a dog? Paul whispered a command to his pet, patted him, and watched him trot off.

The men had finished muffling the oarlocks, the boat was again untied and ready to put off, when the dog came running down the wharf, a pair of spurs jangling at his collar. Either the soldiers had failed to notice the animal on its errand, or they had not been quick enough to catch him.

Murmuring words of praise to his pet, Paul unloosed the spurs and told the dog to go home. Then, silently, the boat pushed off from the shore, into the river.

The Charles had never before looked so wide to Paul! It was high with spring flood, and now the moon bathed the water in a steady light. Paul, who would have been grateful for moonlight on some of his rides, wished desperately that this night were dark.

Between them and the other shore lay the British man-of-war, *Somerset*, its guns pointed. Paul's boat had to pass beneath its very shadow. Straight as a dart, and as fast as two men could row it, the little craft shot across the silver water. It seemed impossible that lookouts aboard the *Somerset* had not spotted them soon after they started. Paul held his breath, and waited for the sound of a gun, a voice shouting halt. Now they were out of the moonlight, in the shadow of the warship. The guns were very close, and surely any one with listening ears could hear the soft slap of the oars, the splash of small waves against the boat.

But they skimmed safely past the *Somerset*, out of the patch of dark water, back into the moonlight. They were still a long way from shore. The men rowed faster now, in a kind of frantic haste. They forgot to be careful as they dipped the oars, letting them splash into the river, because speed seemed more important than silence.

Gradually objects on the Charlestown side began to take shape. Trees became distinct and the Charlestown Battery could be sighted. Back on the *Somerset*, no torches indicated alarm, no guns moved. By some miracle the little boat, skipping across the moonlit water, had not been noticed.

The men pulled the boat up on the shore, and stood for a moment, mopping their brows, thankful for the solid earth beneath their feet.

Then Paul, alone, set out walking rapidly toward town.

In Charlestown he found friends waiting. They had seen the signal lanterns and a good horse was saddled and ready for him.

One of the men said, worriedly, "I just came from up Lexington way this evening. I saw ten British officers riding toward Concord at sundown. Guard carefully, or you may be taken."

Paul answered, "I know of the danger. There's the chance, though, they won't see me in these dark clothes."

"Are you armed?"

"No. I left my pistols home purposely. An armed man, if captured, would certainly be held. Unarmed, they might think me harmless and let me go.

"If I meet the Redcoats," he added, "my only hope is to outwit them or outride them."

CHAPTER TEN

The Midnight Ride

IT was eleven o'clock when Paul left Charlestown and dashed off down the moonlit road. He would take the shortest route to Lexington, and he must ride hard.

Paul wondered if Dawes had been able to get through. He thought about the ten officers his Charlestown friend had seen, and he pushed from his mind the fearful possibility that perhaps Hancock and Adams had already been taken.

A gust of wind started up. The leafing trees cast moving shadows, making a restless pattern of light and dark. And more than once Paul slowed up at a shifting shape, only to find it a trick of the wind and moon.

But now, close beside that tree. Surely that was no illusion? Two men on horseback bolted out of the shadows into his path, and shouted at Paul to halt. Paul could see by the cockades on their hats and the holsters at their sides that they were British officers. One of them rushed on down the road to head Paul off if he should make a dash for it. The other man plunged toward Paul.

Revere wheeled his horse around sharply. There was a crossroad back a piece—if he could only make it, he might lose his pursuer there. Even as he turned, he saw the rider, close beside him, make a dive for his bridle. Paul veered and dodged away from the soldier, and pressed in his spurs, urging his poor beast faster than it could go. He had shaken the Redcoat off all right, now, if he could only outrun him! For the second time that night Paul listened for the sound of shots.

His horse leaped ahead in swift, easy strides, and Paul knew he was outdistancing the officer. However, he was riding away from Lexington, not toward it. And he had no wish to waste time and wear out his horse, racing in the wrong direction. Besides, he did not know his mount. If the chase were a long one, the soldier might well overtake him.

Now, just ahead of him was the crossroad. And above him the rocking trees threw fitful shadows. In the tricky light, he might be able to elude the pursuer.

He turned the horse into the crossroad. The lane ran uphill now and there were no trees to blot out the moonlight. The dark-cloaked rider would make a good target! Paul looked back, wishing he had brought his pistols, for, if shots were going to be fired, he would like to answer them.

But his ruse had worked! Fooled by the shifting light and shadows, the Redcoat had ridden past the crossroad. Even as Paul paused for a second to make sure, the officer realized his blunder and turned to see the dark figure of horse and rider on the crest of the hill, limned against the moonlit sky. He could never catch the rebel by retracing his way. The Redcoat decided on a short cut. He jumped his horse across a low hedge and plunged into the field.

Paul chuckled at what he saw. Beyond the hedge, in the middle of the field, was a clay bog. The horse was in deep; floundering, pitching, trying hopelessly to rear his way out. By the time the poor creature, with his sweating, cursing rider, freed himself, Paul was far out of sight, out of reach. In his relief at escape, he had one regret; he was forced, by his turn at the crossroad, to take a longer route to Lexington, by way of Mistick. He had almost thirteen miles to go. He must ride harder.

At Mistick he stopped just long enough to rouse the Minute Men. Lights flickered in the town, bells began ringing the alarm before Paul was out on the road again.

He halted at every farmhouse, banging loudly on the doors because there was no time for courtesies, shouting his warning to sleepy-headed farmers who were angry, more often than not, at being so rudely awakened. And before the window was closed, the candle lighted, Paul was on his way.

He was fighting, not only against time, but against

capture. There was no turning back now if a Redcoat blocked his way, and his tired horse could never out-distance a fresh mount. So he raced ahead, disregarding shadows that stirred like living figures, refusing to listen for hoofbeats that might be following.

Shortly after midnight, he saw the dim huddle of houses that was Lexington. The Reverend Dr. Clark's home, where Adams and Hancock were staying, looked tranquil in the darkness. Its very stillness told Paul he had come in time.

Paul leaped from his horse and dashed to the door. The thumping of his boots brought a sentry on the run.

"Stop your noise!" the guard hissed. "You'll disturb the whole house."

"Noise!" Paul roared. "You'll have noise enough before long. The Regulars are out!" He brushed the guard aside, and raising his fist thundered at the door.

"Who is it?" Adams called out.

"Revere," Paul shouted.

His name brought the house alive. Candles glimmered, slippered feet pattered through the upstairs halls, men's and women's voices mingled in questions and answers. A shaft of light spread down the stairway, and Adams and Hancock, still in their nightcaps and holding candles high, hurried to let Paul in.

"Sit down, man." Hancock pushed a chair toward Paul. "And now, what is the word?"

"The British are moving," Paul answered. "They

left Boston by boat and are headed this way, sir."

Hancock and Adams sat silent for a moment. From above stairs, where women and servants waited in the darkness, came a flutter of whispers.

"You had no trouble getting through?" Adams asked.

Then Paul, sitting there in the dim light, the house quiet with listening, told them about the officers he had eluded, how he had raised the Minute Men at Mistick and shouted a warning at every house from there on to Lexington.

Paul asked, "You've heard nothing from William Dawes? He was dispatched a little earlier than I, to ride by way of Boston Neck."

The question was scarcely voiced when a horse and rider raced up to the house, and William Dawes was welcomed in.

He, too, had warned every house and hamlet on his way. And now, with Paul, he was ready to go on to Concord.

As they left, they heard Sam Adams shout to the guard, "Set the alarm bells ringing, rouse the people. The British are on the march!"

It was six miles to Concord. The two men, riding side by side, hurried their tired horses. Paul told Dawes of the ten British officers his Charlestown friend had seen riding toward Concord some hours before. Paul added, "After dark, likely, the men would pair off to spread out their guard. We may well be stopped."

From behind them came the clatter of hooves. They spurred their animals on, but both men knew their horses were too tired for a race. Closer, closer, the sound came. Paul looked back. It was a single rider. And Paul breathed a sigh of relief to see he wore no cockade on his hat, no sign of military apparel.

The man overtook them easily. "Are you headed for Concord?" Paul asked.

"Yes," the stranger answered, "I live there. My name's Samuel Prescott."

"Prescott!" Paul was glad to hear the name. He knew of the man as prominent Son of Liberty in Concord.

"I'm Revere, and this is William Dawes. We've ridden express from Boston tonight—the British are moving toward Lexington and Concord. Are you out on an errand for the Sons?"

"No," Prescott laughed, "I'm not. I've been calling on a young lady. But if you'll let me go with you, I'll be proud." He added eagerly, "I know this countryside, every field, every wood, each turn in the road, every home and who lives there."

"You'll be good assistance," Paul answered. "Besides, your horse is rested. If we're trapped, your chance of escape is better than ours."

Paul told him then the exact message that was to be carried to Concord and how every household must be roused.

They sped along, pounding on doors, crying out the alarm. One mile, two miles, three miles—half way to Concord!

Just ahead were three farmhouses, dark and sleeping. "We'd better separate, to save time." Paul directed.

Prescott said, "The one on the right is deserted."

"You and Dawes take the first house, then, I'll ride on to the place up the road." And Paul was off alone.

He hadn't gone two hundred yards when suddenly, from the shadows, plunged two riders; British officers with pistols ready. Paul shouted a warning to his companions, but they were already riding rapidly toward him. Just as they reached Paul, two more soldiers slipped from the darkness, forming a barrier across the road.

In spite of the drawn swords and pistols, Revere and his friends tried to ride past the soldiers. But one of them headed Paul off, and pointing a gun at his heart, spit out an oath and said, "If you go an inch farther, you're a dead man." Dawes and Prescott, too, were surrounded. With their tired, nervous horses pawing and snorting, they were herded into a small field.

But each of the three men was thinking fast. Dawes was remembering the deserted farmhouse. Prescott knew that beyond the fence at the back of the field lay smooth hard earth and clear meadowland to Lincoln, then a back road to Concord.

Paul noticed the wood on his right. His horse was too tired for a chase, but if he could once gain the protection of the trees, he might play a game of hide-and-seek and come out winner!

"Put on!" It was young Prescott's shout. His horse pitched back, and before the startled British knew what was happening, he had skimmed across the field, cleared the fence and was away. In the excitement Paul bolted for the woods, Dawes cut across field, gained the road, and headed for the deserted farmhouse. There were two Britishers close after Dawes. He had no chance to outrun them. But with true Yankee shrewdness, he could outwit them. The Redcoats were at his heels when he reached the empty house. Dawes shouted at the blank windows, "Come on out, boys, I've got two of them!"

And the Redcoats, thinking they'd been tricked into an ambush, retreated speedily, hurrying back to their comrades down the road. Dawes was cut off from Concord, but he had, at least, escaped.

But Paul! He had no sooner gained the protection of the trees than six officers, in hiding there, surrounded him, grabbed his bridle, and with pistols pressed against him, ordered him to dismount.

They led Paul and his horse back to the open space where his first captors waited.

Guns aimed, they began to question him. "Where are you from?"

Paul hesitated, and the major leaned from his horse and placed his pistol against Paul's head. "Now answer truthfully," he commanded, "and don't try to run. One move and I'll blow your brains out. From where have you ridden and when did you leave?"

"I left Boston at about eleven o'clock, this night," Paul answered.

The major exclaimed in surprise, "You must have ridden hard, my man, and with a purpose. Boston is a good distance." And then he asked, "Who are you?"

Paul might as well tell the truth, for if they discovered him in a lie, they would certainly shoot him as a spy. But with sheer audacity he might out-bluff them.

"Revere," he answered.

"Revere!" Several of the Redcoats blurted the name in surprise. "Not *Paul* Revere?"

"Yes, Paul Revere of Boston."

Some of the soldiers cursed him for his boldness. One raised his bayonet as if to strike. But the major said, "Don't abuse him. This is a fine capture we've made, and he'll be less valuable dead than alive."

Paul said brashly, "If you're heading for the stores at Concord, sir, you've missed your aim."

"Be silent!" the major growled. "We've no such plan. We were at the road here only waiting to pick up some deserters when you came along."

Paul knew, of course, there was no truth in his words. He stood there, the soldiers on their mounts tall above him, swords and pistols fencing him in. And his very position, on the ground at the feet of the Redcoats' horses, filled him with a sudden rage.

"I know what you're after!" he cried. "Deserters be plagued! I saw your men load into boats off Boston Common this very night. But they'll never get here!" In his fury he thought up a magnificent lie. "They're aground—all fifteen hundred of them. Aground in passing the river."

"You lie!"

"Furthermore, I've alarmed the country the whole way up. There are five hundred Minute Men gathered right now in Lexington, and more coming!"

"Gad! The fellow may be telling the truth," a lieutenant ventured.

"Mount your horse," the major ordered Paul. And added sarcastically, "We'll take you to your friends." Paul supposed he meant Adams and Hancock.

The Redcoats formed a box around him, so there was no possible way of escape. Paul reached for his bridle, but the major knocked it out of his hand and said, "Drop your bridle! You'll have no command over your horse. The sergeant will lead you."

So they started for Lexington, with a roll of hoofbeats, swords silver in the moonlight; a square of crimson coats and bright cockades with one black figure in the center.

They had almost reached Lexington when they heard the ringing of a bell.

"What is that?" the major asked.

"It's the alarm bell, atop the Lexington Meeting-house," Paul answered.

The Redcoats seemed disturbed, but they jogged on. Soon they could see that the town was filled with lights. Signal fires glowed on the hilltops, torches were held high in the streets, and every window shone with candle gleam.

There was a hushed conference between the major and his chief officer, and the horses slowed up. But apparently the major was not to be frightened by mere bell ringing and firelight, for they moved on.

Almost into town they were, when a burst of shooting split the air. The horses were pulled up short. Paul recognized the sound as a signal, fired probably from the Tavern. But the major hurriedly withdrew his men, and Paul, into the shelter of a wall close to a small, dark graveyard.

"How far is it to Cambridge?" he demanded roughly of Paul.

Paul told him.

The major turned to his sergeant, who rode a very small mount, and asked, "Is your horse tired?"

"Yes, sir."

"Then take this man's horse." He nudged Paul with his gun, and Paul dismounted. They took the saddle and bridle off the small, weary horse of the sergeant, gave her a spank, and set her off down the road, riderless.

Paul felt sorry for his own exhausted beast when he saw the big man swing onto her back. But in another second, the major issued a sharp command, and the officers were off toward Cambridge.

Paul stood for a second, stunned with the surprise of suddenly being alone. Then he started on a run, across the graveyard, toward the home of Dr. Clark.

Hancock and Adams were still there, dressed and armed, and debating whether to leave Lexington or not. Paul told them his story. He was fairly sure that Prescott had managed to reach Concord.

"But," he turned to the two patriots, "the British officers were abusive, sir. I fear if they should return and find you here, their treatment would be rough."

The Reverend Jonas Clark spoke, "It's said that Gage believes if they capture you, Boston can easily be subjected. It is foolish for you to risk being taken."

And so it was decided that Hancock and Adams would go on to a house in Woburn, two miles from Lexington, and Revere should accompany them.

Since Paul had no horse, and the beasts available were heavily laden, he walked. He could not remember how long it had been since he'd had a complete rest.

He arrived at the Woburn house, dead tired, to find a turmoil of excitement. A trunk of papers, important papers, belonging to Hancock had been left behind at the Tavern in Lexington. It was essential for these not to fall into British hands.

Hancock's secretary, Lowell, said, "It's my place to go back for them."

"I'll go with you," Paul offered, "it's too great a burden for one man."

The two men set out, walking. When they reached Lexington the russet glow of the signal fires was staining the first silver of dawn. The meetinghouse green was covered with Minute Men, boys too young for fighting, old men in thin clothes, strapping young farmers dressed for spring plowing. They stood in ragged lines, waiting.

Paul and Lowell went up to the chamber in the tavern where the trunk was hidden. They sat down for a moment to rest before starting back with their load. Paul looked out of the window. In the faint light he saw red lines filling the road. They moved in rhythm, and steadily closer, with steps keeping time to the beat of drums.

"The British have come to Lexington," he said. "We must be off."

Hurrying with the trunk, the men passed the green where the soldiers waited for the British. Paul heard their captain, John Parker, say to the Minute Men, "Let the troops pass by. Don't molest them unless they begin first."

Paul and his companion crossed the road and set the trunk down, pausing a moment to look back. The British troops were approaching the green. They made a short halt in front of the Minute Men.

Paul thought of the captain's warning . . . let the troops pass by. . . . Lexington was quiet as death. Then breaking the stillness was the crack of a pistol. A wisp of gray smoke rose in front of the Colonial militia. The British had fired.

An angry shout rose from the Minute Men. Paul saw the ragged lines break, the men run a few paces forward. Then the burst of gunfire shut out all other sounds.

Paul started suddenly, as if to join them. He stopped, turned and picked up the trunk for which Hancock was anxiously waiting.

All the way back to Woburn he saw roads crowded with those in flight. Mothers with babies in their arms; children, too small for the bundles they carried, tagging along; old people hobbling behind, waving the younger ones on. Women stopped in the growing light to spade holes in which they buried their keepsakes and silver. In deserted farmyards stood cows wanting milking, and frightened sheep fled over the partly plowed fields.

The shot had been fired that was heard round the world. The war had begun.

CHAPTER ELEVEN

Farewell to Boston

FOR Paul to return to Boston now would mean death. The British lay in wait for men like him. They had already arrested poor Robert Newman, on suspicion that he was the man who had hung the signal lanterns in North Church. Paul, who was known to have carried the alarm, would be strung up on sight.

But back in Boston was his family—Rachel with the children and a five-month-old baby to care for. And Boston, in a state of siege, was no pleasant place.

The British were in high temper. They had marched into Lexington that dawn so jauntily, their fifes whistling, their soldiers arrogant. But before the sun set they sang another tune.

The Colonists, whom they had expected to scatter like leaves, had pushed the British back. It was a kind of warfare new to the Redcoats. Bullets came from nowhere. Deserted houses suddenly sprung guns, forcing them farther in their retreat. If the soldiers halted, muskets roared from an empty field to hurry them. Colonists ambushed them from behind fence posts, rained bullets from trees. And the British, seeing no army, could not fight.

On and on they were pushed back. No time to rest, no time to bury their dead. Finally, on reaching Charlestown, they had small choice but to scurry into Boston and hold it in siege.

The King's army was locked in the city. No one could come in. Nobody could get out.

Now, from the country north of Boston, and all the land around, came farmers, fishermen, preachers and teachers, storekeepers and schoolboys, ready to fight. Word of the war spread as if carried by the winds. Before nightfall on the second day the hills around the besieged town were covered with rude camps to shelter the gathering army.

They dared not fire on the British in Boston, for the city was still filled with their own people. But let Gage and his men come out!

In the meantime Paul waited in Charlestown for further orders and prayed for news of his family. It was certain that the people in Boston were suffering from lack of food, for the town was shut so tight not even provisions could be taken in.

At last came word that Gage had agreed to let non-combatants leave if they deposited any weapons they owned with him.

Paul sat down then and penned a letter to Rachel. He knew the man who ran the Charlestown-Boston ferry. If he would take it across, it might reach her. At least, he must try to let her know where he was. And if he couldn't come to her, she and the children would have to come to him.

Carefully he wrote explicit directions—". . . send beds enough for yourself and children, my chest, your trunk, with books, clothes, etc., to the ferry. Tell the ferryman they are mine. I will provide a house here and be here to receive them. . . . Then come with the children, all except Paul——"

Those last words must have been hard for Paul to write. His boy was only fifteen, hardly old enough to be left in a besieged city with the responsibility of guarding his father's shop and the family home.

Paul thought a moment before sealing Rachel's letter, then added this postscript to young Paul:

My Son

It is now in your power to be serviceable to me, your mother and yourself. I beg you to keep yourself at home or where your Mother sends you. Don't come away till I send you word. When you bring anything to the ferry, tell them it is mine and mark it with my name.

Your loving father.

Scarcely had the letter gone when rumors spread that Gage, having collected all the available weapons from those eager to leave the city, had refused to let the people go.

But as day followed day, and the food grew scarcer, the general saw his men become surly with hunger.

Better to let some of the people leave. There would be more food for the soldiers.

So Gage issued an order that people could leave the city after getting a proper pass. But they could take no provisions, no food, nothing but necessary household goods and their own clothes.

Rachel hated to beg a favor of the British, but it meant seeing Paul and having the children in a safer place. So she swallowed her pride and went to ask for a pass.

The pass was promised. Rachel came home to gather together their things and wait.

The Revere house was in a state of mad confusion. Winter clothes, quilts and coverlets, hung out in the spring sunshine for an airing before they were packed. "We must take them," Rachel explained. "Winter may come and go before we see Boston again. Besides, nothing may be left when we get back."

The rugs were rolled up, iron pots piled, dishes in barrels, clothes folded in boxes. But still the pass was not granted.

Other people were getting passes. Every hour saw carts, stacked high with household goods, roll out of Boston. And every day some neighbor came to make an unhappy farewell, brave but anxious people, closing doors of homes that might not be there when they returned.

Paul, on the Charlestown side, saw the loaded carts

come over the ferry, and fumed because his own things were not among them. Rachel had written that a pass was expected hourly. What in thunder was causing the delay?

And then suddenly it occurred to him: perhaps the soldiers were waiting for a bribe! Paul grew angry at the thought, but the suspense of waiting for his family was becoming too great. With what should he bribe them? Money? Money was of little use in Boston; there was nothing there to buy. Food? That was it. The poor devils were probably hungry.

The bribe would have to be offered by some one whom he could trust. Paul finally decided to write Rachel and have her tell the sergeant of the guard at the ferry that, as soon as she was given a pass, Mr. Revere would send over beef and veal for him and his men.

Again Rachel put on her shawl and bonnet, and, with her head held high, went to speak to the Red-coats.

The mention of meat was magic. A few days later a messenger came to the Revere door with word that the pass was ready and waiting.

Young Paul ran to hire a dray-cart. The other children carried out bundles and boxes to load. Rachel flew about the dismantled house, making sure nothing important had been forgoten.

There was a keg of sugar, a sack of meal, one side

of bacon. How she regretted leaving these! Money would be scarce, food short.

"We could hide the bacon in the barrel with the kitchen things," young Paul whispered the suggestion.

Rachel hesitated for a moment. Then she shook her head. "No, we daren't take the chance."

She glanced through the house then for the last time. In the back yard the gardens were newly green. The heartsease was budding, the lilacs starting to bloom. She closed the kitchen door on these, bolted it. She tried each window to make sure it was fastened. The rooms looked strange without their plump white beds and bright rugs. With a sinking heart she realized that soon soldiers would plunder through, searching for loot. But the knowledge that in another hour she would see Paul gave her courage.

He was waiting, of course, when the boat bumped to a stop on the Charleston shore. His anxious eyes had picked out his little group, long before the ferry came to a standstill. There was Rachel, smiling, the young baby in her arms, the little girls clustered about her.

The children ran off the boat, joyfully, toward their father. He took time to kiss them, every one. Then he hurried to Rachel and lifted the baby gently from her arms.

He knew they would not be together for long. But this was a happy moment for all of them.

CHAPTER TWELVE

Money and Gunpowder

EVERY day, since the first shot was fired, Paul had expected orders sending him to war. He had been eager for action, especially after his family was sheltered in Charleston.

But now, instead of cleaning his musket and filling his powder horn, he was sitting in Charlestown, worried about getting his graving tools smuggled out of Boston and trying to figure out how to rig up a printing press.

For the colonies needed money. The only way they had of getting some was to print it, and Paul was the logical craftsman for them to turn to for help.

One by one the tools were slipped onto the ferry— hidden in bedding, stuffed in a shirt front, wedged in with some good housewife's cook pots. Across the river to Charlestown and Paul. Then, after the tools, came his copper engravings. He could get no new copper for the plates, so he would have to engrave the money on the backs of his old cartoons and Boston scenes.

Piece by piece a makeshift press was put together, and Paul was ready to begin work.

It irked him, though, this business of sitting there in the kitchen, scratching pictures on copper, when other men were marching by, off to rout the British.

"Most men can fire a gun," Rachel would soothe his impatience. "You're needed for more important things."

Paul would look up from his work of creating our country's first money, and say, "It's hard for a strong man to be content at a workbench with all of Massachusetts up in arms."

"For my part, I'm thankful to have you where I can speak your name and hear you answer," Rachel said, "you'll be in danger soon enough."

But throughout the summer Paul was kept busy printing the currency. Sometimes, in order that soldiers could be paid, he worked at the press day and night, without sleep or rest. Trusted Continental officers guarded him at his work.

Rachel's prophecy of danger did not come true until fall.

Toward the end of summer the Continental Army began to run out of gunpowder. George Washington wrote in alarm to Congress. The precious stores that had looked so important were almost exhausted. Members of Congress gathered in anxious consultations.

"What can we do?" The question was asked in panic, and nobody had an answer.

Before the war gunpowder had been brought over

from England. Now, of course, that source was closed.
Once upon a time a few powder mills had been oper-
ated in the colonies. But these lay in ruins, long since
abandoned, because of the restrictions placed on them
by the mother country. With the crumbling of the
mills was lost the secret of making the powder.

There were rumors that colonial troops, with empty
guns, were facing British fire. Paul knew for a fact
that the thirteen-mile chain of sentries so bravely en-
circling Boston, had no ammunition. With pointed
guns they dared Gage to come out, and held the Redcoats back, but they could not have fired at them. How
long would it be until the British suspected those colonial muskets were empty?

Word came that there was a small powder mill in
operation near Philadelphia. Its owner, Oswell Eve,
knew the magic of making the explosive. He could
supply some of the troops, in that section. But another
mill—a big mill—had to be started at once in New
England. Some one must go to the Philadelphia mill
and learn how to make powder.

So, on a blustery November day, Paul set out for
Philadelphia to see Mr. Eve.

Through sleety rains, over half-frozen roads, he
traveled the three hundred and fifty-six long miles.
He had not only bad roads and weather to worry about,
but capture by the British. Sudden bends in his path
he must take cautiously. A pounding of hoof-beats sent

him into the shadows, watchful, waiting, until he made sure who came. He was impatient at these time-stealing delays, but he dared not risk being taken.

Then, late one morning, and with an icy wind driving him, he rode safely into Philadelphia. He stopped first for credentials from members of the Continental Congress. Mr. Eve must understand that this was a patriotic undertaking, done in the name of Liberty, and not a private, money-making scheme.

The plumes of smoke from the powder mill's chimneys told Paul it was busy. He tied up his horse and knocked at the door.

To the fellow who answered Paul said, "I'd like to see Mr. Oswell Eve. I'm Paul Revere, and come with credentials from the Continental Congress."

The fellow closed the door without so much as inviting Paul in, and disappeared.

The wind grew ever colder, and Paul would have been obliged for an invitation to wait inside. But after a few minutes the door opened again, and Eve came out, slamming it behind him.

Paul told him why he had come, and showed him the letter from Congress. Eve read it, folded it carefully and handed it back to Paul. He said sullenly, "I'm making gunpowder for the soldiers."

Paul looked puzzled. "That I know. But one mill cannot supply them all, sir."

"I would be a stupid man," Eve said slowly, "to

give away the secret by which I make my living."

Paul was stunned by this attitude. "But, my good fellow, a powder mill in Massachusetts can't in any way interfere with your business here," he pleaded.

"To argue with me about it is useless. I'll keep my secret to myself."

Paul fought to control the anger that made him want to throttle the mill-owner. He said, "I am here not as a man who wants to become a competitor, but as one who knows that we have soldiers fighting British fire with stones and hunting-knives because they are out of powder. It's for the cause of Freedom, not profit, I beg your help."

Eve shook his head stubbornly, and Paul could see he cared little who won the war, so long as he sold the powder.

Paul made a last gamble. "If you won't let me stay and learn your trade, would you at least permit me to come in for a few moments and warm myself? I've ridden ten days, through sleet and mud to reach you."

Eve hesitated, then a little flicker of shame crossed his face, and he opened the door and let Paul in. Certainly no one could learn anything important about his process in a few moments' looking.

Paul stamped his feet to warm them. He took off his greatcoat, stiff with frost, and put it before the fire. He chatted with Eve about the weather, about the wax museum so famous in Philadelphia, about taverns and food and the condition of roads. Eve spoke little. But the conversation gave Paul time.

For while he talked Paul's eyes took in every corner of the mill. And when Eve was busy, Paul wandered about, apparently aimlessly, but packing his head with mental notes.

That would be saltpeter there, sulphur in the sack, charcoal beside it. All had been reduced to a fine powder, but he recognized them. Great kettles were filled with a doughlike mixture. Water as a moistener, Paul thought, for no other liquid was about.

He saw a large wooden box about eighteen inches deep—his eyes measured it—and five feet square. And beside it a set of sieves. He counted them quickly—five sieves of varying coarseness. The contraption looked much like a wheat riddle, he noted, only the sieves were more finely screened.

There a man was pounding the dough mixture in a mortar. At one end of the mill a barrel was turning slowly—probably reducing the mixture to dust, Paul thought. Now that door—what was behind it? He loitered along until a workman opened it, and quickly closed it behind him. But in that second Paul's eyes had seen a small room heated by a stove with trays of gunpowder drying.

He said good-bye to Mr. Eve and thanked him. He climbed on his horse and rode rapidly until he was out of sight. Then he took paper and a plummet from his

Eve refuses to give away his secrets

pocket and quickly sketched everything he had seen, jotted down all the information he had deduced.

It would take some dangerous experimenting. But Paul believed he had learned Eve's carefully guarded secret.

On the way back, even greater care had to be taken against capture. If the British caught him now, they would certainly search him. Plans for a powder mill would be ugly evidence.

When the rain turned to snow, and riders came upon him suddenly out of the white blur, Paul rode with a prayer on his lips. He forced himself to stop when the early winter darkness settled, and not to start until after daybreak. And during the too few daylight hours, he rode almost without pause and never relaxed his watch.

So he made the tedious journey back.

An old wreck of a powder mill at Canton, Massachusetts, was rebuilt for Paul's experiments. In his various other work he had learned enough chemistry and mechanics to know what he was about.

Even so, batch after batch of powder was made only to fail when tested.

"That lot needed more pounding in the mortar," Paul would say, or, "I should have dried it longer." Again, "Too much sulphur, not enough charcoal—that batch should have been screened more finely."

Each failure taught him something.

While the experiments were going on, poor Rachel, waiting in Charlestown, spent sleepless nights and worried days.

Working with gunpowder was, in itself, a dangerous undertaking. She knew that a tiny spark could send the mill to the clouds, and Paul with it. Furthermore, if the British heard of the enterprise, they would surely try to blow it to bits.

But the experiments went on. Finally, one day, Paul tested a measure of his powder and found it perfect! Word of his success spread in excited whispers. Soldiers were given new hope, their leaders planned new campaigns. Other powder mills now could be started to supply the Continental Army. Their muskets need no longer be empty.

His hazardous and important venture finished, Paul handed the secrets and the work of powder making over to other men.

He was going to war!

CHAPTER THIRTEEN

Paul Revere, Colonel

PAUL had never seen a more tattered and miserable collection of soldiers. He had been made their lieutenant-colonel, and the post, he knew, would be a hard one.

He and his men were stationed at bleak Fort William, on Castle Island in Boston Bay. There, surrounded by the gray water and drenched in fog, they took up the monotonous burden of guarding the forts in the harbor. For under Paul's command was the harbor and all that was in it: island garrisons, the anchored boats, ships that moved, British vessels to be held as prizes of war.

Now began the hard years; years of bitter winters and hunger, of dying men and men going mad with suffering and despair.

Paul saw his soldiers marching in bare feet over the frozen ground. He saw them sleeping in zero weather with no blankets to cover them and their clothes threadbare. All of them were hungry. And he knew, as they did, that many of their families were starving because the soldier-fathers had received no pay for months on end.

So—in addition to all his other duties—he waged a

constant, desperate fight for shoes and coats, blankets, shirts, food and pay. Dabs of supplies would come. But there was never enough to go around.

Sometimes, on a dark night, Paul would hear the splash of a body in water, and he would know that another of his men, frantic with need, was deserting. Once in a while, out of the darkness, he would hear a shouted alarm, then silence, and an empty sentry post would tell him that another soldier had been high-jacked by privateers.

As the ranks were thinned by death and desertion and kidnapping, other men came to fill the empty places. Each fresh group of volunteers was younger than the last, until it seemed that soon even the children would go to war. And one day when new contingents came to join Revere's half-starved, half-naked forces, his own son was among them, young Paul, just sixteen.

It mattered little that no one was left in charge of the Revere shop. People were too poor and too busy with war to think of silver teapots and golden buckles.

Women of New England, instead of planning new silver services, were melting up their pewter spoons and porringers to make bullets for the soldiers. Now in place of quilting bees and candy pulls, they gave bullet parties. Each guest brought her cherished pewter, and while some melted it down and poured it into bullet moulds, others made wooden dishes to replace the pewter. Wooden bowls and plates tediously scraped with broken glass, they were, and polished to fine smoothness with limestone.

The soldiers, shivering in their rude shelters or clustered about meager campfires, thirsted for news from those they'd left behind. When news came from their women folks, it was mostly war news. Houses burned, cattle stolen, another yard of cloth woven for soldiers' breeches, another measure of grain ground for soldiers' meal.

New recruits brought fresh stories for the men to hear. And these, too, were of the war. Sad stories and funny stories, stories of triumphs and defeats, but always of the war.

"Down New York way," one man told it, "a party of young ladies—and nice, proper girls they were, too—got hold of a fellow who'd poked fun at the Continental Army. They stripped him to the waist, and smeared him good with molasses. Then they dumped a pillow full of feathers over his head. He was a pretty sight going home!"

The men all laughed.

"Women folks aren't much for shootin'" one of the men observed, "but they're a heap o' help in fighting a war just the same. A fellow from down south told me 'bout a girl—a pretty girl—who offered to carry a message the army had to get through British lines. She pinned the papers under one of her petticoats.

"Well, the British caught her. They locked her up, on suspicion, and went to get a woman to search her. While they were gone, she read the message and memorized it, then ate the paper. Ate very scrap of it, ink and all! A woman came back with the soldiers, and searched her, but she couldn't find a thing. So they let her go—and the girl got through with the message in her head."

The soldiers nodded their approval, and another spoke. "Talk about good women and smart women, there's a lady over near Dedham, right here in Massachusetts, does a fine thing. She's turned her kitchen over to bread-baking. Day and night she's got pans of bread going in and coming out of the oven.

"In front of her house, beside the road, a long table is set up. She keeps it spread with loaves of hot bread and pots of cheese and tubs of cider for passing soldiers. She says, 'I don't want any fighting man to pass by my house hungry or thristy.' Works day and night."

"Is that the truth?" The half-starved men were incredulous.

"Sure it's true," another man put in, "I saw it. I stopped and had me some. Best bread I ever tasted. And nobody can say where she gets all the flour."

"Hummm," a man said hungrily, "I'm goin' to head straight for Dedham!"

Paul was glad when the men took up time with talk. It helped them forget their miseries. When Paul had time, he listened too. Sometimes their stories stirred old memories.

Once a man bragged, "I was in New York, right there at Bowling Green, when the boys tore the King's statue down. Tumbled it right into the street, they did, and kicked it around. Now it's been melted up to make bullets for the Continental Army." Paul remembered his first glimpse of the statue, how he came upon it in the wintry twilight while he was watching for landmarks that would lead him to the home of John Lamb.

Then a boy, not to be outdone by the man's experience, spoke up, "I was in Boston when the British chopped down the Liberty Tree. They had to take turns chopping, and it took 'em half the night. Said it was the toughest tree they'd ever seen anywhere."

Paul thought of the patriotic rallies the Sons had held under the old tree. He recollected the night they'd hung the effigy of the stamp collector from its branches. Essex Street would seem strange with the scarred stump in place of the great elm.

"Pure meanness, cuttin' down that tree," a man said slowly. "First settlers planted that tree, and it was a hundred and thirty years old. Pure meanness."

But Paul, looking at the dying campfire, knowing of the dwindling supply of wood, wondered if the British soldiers, during the siege of Boston, might not have been cold too. The elm must have made a fine lot of fuel.

Once in a great while Paul was able to leave his regiment and go home for a short, precious visit with Rachel and the children. There, too, fuel and food were scarce. But they were all grateful for what they had, and those brief reunions were the only happy times in Paul's three bleak years at Fort William.

Back with his men, faced again with the problems and sufferings of war, he could remember the kitchen with the firelight glowing on the children's faces and Rachel smiling from across the table. And the room redolent with food smells—potatoes roasting in the hot ashes, flounder browning in the iron skillet. He could hear Rachel's soft laughter as she poured out a steaming pot of makeshift tea brewed from dried raspberry leaves—hyperion tea they called it. Even the children pretended to like it, for it was all they had to drink. These and many other things he remembered during the gray days and bitter nights when he was too tired to rest, too cold to sleep.

Only twice was he ordered to leave the island with a body of troops for action on the mainland. Once in the capacity of military police, he and a force marched to Worcester to take charge of the Hessians captured in the battle of Bennington. And once he and his men were sent to Rhode Island to help drive the British from Newport.

Paul's part in the war ended when he was sent on the futile Penobscot expedition after his work at the fort was over.

If there had been any glory to the war, any gran-
deur, he had not seen it. He had seen sickness and
hunger and misery, and brave men dying the same
death as the cowards.

His friend, John Warren, lay in a shallow grave,
shot to death at Bunker Hill. Young Samuel Prescott,
who had ridden with him so boldly toward Concord
that April night, was dead in the squalor of a British
prison camp. These were but two.

And what of the Redcoats who had come, so spir-
ited, so sure? In the harbor, under Paul's command,
what was left of their defeated regiments waited on
transports for orders to return home. Before they
sailed Paul received this note:

> The British Officers in general and Captain O'Connell
> in particular present their compliments to Colonel Re-
> vere, and beg the favor of his company to take a glass
> of wine before their departure. . . .

Thus, gallantly, those who lost paid tribute to a
victor who had treated them fairly.

The British, too, were going back to their homes
with their maimed and their sick and their messages
of death. And for them there was no victory to lighten
the sorrows.

The war had had to be fought. Paul was sure of
that. But liberty was hard-won and the price of freedom high.

CHAPTER FOURTEEN

The Return Home

THE Boston Paul and his family returned to was a sad place.

Half its population had disappeared during the Revolution. Of the many who had fled at the time of the siege, some would return. But there were thousands of others who would never come back: sons and fathers lost in battle, drowned at sea; women and children who died of hunger or exposure or in the smallpox plagues that had swept the city.

Paul saw their homes deserted and shabby, windows broken, roofs sagging. He saw streets, once busy with peddlers' cries and neighbors' talk, now quiet, and weeds growing where the carts had run.

He walked about the town, his heart heavy at the damage he encountered and the familiar faces he missed. Here and there charred remnants of a building showed that fire, too, had taken its toll.

He wandered over to the Common—once Boston's pride—and found it a waste of stumps. The lime trees and elms, so lovingly planted, had been hacked down to provide fuel. The thick lawns were trampled to mud where tents had been pitched and soldiers drilled.

He looked in the window of a deserted church, and saw that the pews had been chopped out—hauled away for firewood when the trees were gone. Shops he remembered as flourishing were closed. Schools were locked and powdery with dust. Gardens were choked out and taken over by the weeds.

Paul walked down to the water front. Neglected boats rotted at the empty piers. In some places the wharves had been torn down, these too used for fuel during the siege. Those left standing were crumbling, and, where exciting cargoes had once been stacked, rats now scurried among the rubbish. Everywhere Paul looked he saw desolation.

He went home sadly, and said to Rachel, "It will take a hundred years to rebuild Boston."

Rachel, remembering how long it takes to grow a tree, nodded.

At the Revere home, another baby boy had been born while Paul was away at war. Paul named him Joseph Warren, for his friend who fell at Bunker Hill.

Paul, with his ever-growing family, buckled down now to the job of re-establishing his business in a bankrupt town. Once again, he made anything and sold everything that people would buy. He forged iron door hinges and thumb catches, locks and knockers. In one corner of his shop, he even put in a small stock of hosiery and several bolts of yard goods. If a man, coming in for a hinge, needed a pair of hose, Paul might just as well sell it to him.

Paul built a little workshop in back of his home, so that at night he could work at his silversmithing without being away from his family. Young Paul worked beside his father now, and Paul was proud of his son, just as his own father had been proud of him.

Silver was scarce. So the Reveres would melt up used metals in order to make new things. They used broken spoons, spectacle frames, old buckles. Paul even took gold and silver lace, ripped off ladies' outmoded gowns, and patiently melted out the metal for bracelets and christening cups.

Bit by bit, little by little, he built up his business. At the same time, Boston set about the heavy task of reconstruction. Wharves were repaired, trees planted again in the Common, houses, schools and churches put in condition for use.

Once again ships sailed into Boston harbor but they carried foreign flags, and they were loaded with things to sell. They had not come to buy.

Paul saw this. He would say, "Winning the war is not enough. We may be free politically but we are still dependent on England and other countries for the things we use."

And as time went on and more ships came, Paul would warn, "Our own fleets are scattered and lost. We have no trade. Our government can't endure unless we learn to make things we now buy."

With this in mind, Paul enlarged his business. "We must have a bigger shop," he would plan. "We must build a small foundry. Iron bolts are needed, spikes and nails—our new country is growing."

Rachel would gasp at his daring. In those uncertain post-war days she watched him borrow to expand, stake everything on a new process, go into debt to build an additional furnace for the output of needed metal.

The Revere family, too, grew during those years. When Joseph Warren was still a small child, a baby sister, Harriet, was born. And the following year, on Christmas Day, Rachel bore another son. Again, it seemed there was always a baby at the Revere house. The cradle that had rocked each of them was seldom empty.

And when there came to be so many of them that they fairly overflowed the little house on North Street, he and Rachel said farewell to the home where they had spent so many happy years, where all of their babies had been born, and moved into a larger place on Charter Street.

Paul was proud of his family. He was happy to see his boys and girls growing up, strong and capable.

He was proud of his shop, too. It was expanded now to include a foundry and glowing furnaces, where he cast anything from a small bolt to a large cannon.

"Each new thing we make," he would say, "is one less item for us to buy abroad."

One day Paul saw a crew of men hoisting a tremendous object from a British sailing ship. It was very heavy, and yet apparently it was fragile. For, while the men strained at the thick hauling ropes, sweating and grunting with the effort, they shouted words of caution to each other and handled the awkward bulk with great care.

Paul knew the men were unloading a bell. This bell, like most of the bells used in the colonies, was cast in England.

Paul had always loved bells. He was a member of the guild that had charge of the eight-bell chime of Christ Church. He could identify every bell in Boston by its sound. He realized, too, how important bells were in everyday life, and he loved them because they were both beautiful and useful.

People lived by bells, for clocks were scarce. The ringing of bells told them it was time to get up in the morning. The bells rang out the noon hour. They called people to church, to public meetings, and told the children when to start for school. A man could tell it was bedtime by the ringing of the bells, and when tragedies of hurricane or fires struck, bells gave out the alarm. To every one Paul knew, the ringing of the bells was important. Each parish, each community, no matter how small, had to have a bell.

Paul watched, thoughtfully, as the men hauled the bell along the wharf and hoisted it onto the padded bed of a sturdy wagon.

He said to himself, "A good lot of money was sent to England to fetch that bell here. It must weigh a thousand pounds."

He thought of the bells he had made: tinkling sleigh bells, dainty bells for dinner tables, cowbells with iron clappers, silvery bells for carriages. None of them weighed as much as a pound; none of them cost as much as a dollar.

The wagon went slowly off with its heavy load. Paul walked behind it, and toward home. A dream, a plan, was taking shape in his head. Would people trust him to do it? He wondered, would Rachel think him foolish?

CHAPTER FIFTEEN

Paul Revere, Bell Maker

PAUL was busy building a large sand pile at his foundry in Lynn Street. The mound of sand was bell-shaped, packed down and baked until it was hard as stone.

Meanwhile, in the foundry, a great iron mold, just a little larger than the sand bell, was being pounded and beaten into shape. Together these would make the form in which Paul would pour hundreds of pounds of molten metal for the casting of his first large bell.

The New Brick Church had made Paul's dream come true. When the church's bell cracked, and a new one was needed, Paul pleaded for a chance to cast it.

Some said, "Revere can make rods and iron bolts and cannons. But a bell is different."

Others argued, "Paul has never failed in any undertaking, and Boston needs to build new industries. Let him try."

So work on the bell began. The foundry now was in a constant hubbub. From dawn until dark there was the ringing of hammers, the glow of the furnaces, clouds of heat rising from the caldrons of melting metal.

When the day came for the bell to be cast, spectators jammed into the foundry to watch Paul and his helpers spill the liquid metal into the mold.

After the bell was cast, it took several days for it to cool. People trooped in and out of the shop to visit the bell, marveling at the amount of heat it radiated, making guesses about its size, its weight, its tone.

Paul watched over it as anxiously as a cook tends a wedding cake that's in the oven. Was it cooling too fast? Or, perhaps, too slowly? Suppose it had cracked in the cooling! Rachel thought she'd never seen Paul so fidgety and worried.

At last, one morning, Paul decided it was time to lift the mold away. It was a tense moment at the foundry. But there was the bell, smooth, flawless and shining.

Proudly Paul read the words stamped on it: *The First Bell Cast in Boston, 1792, P. Revere.* He polished it till it gleamed. The iron clapper he had forged was carefully balanced in it, and the bell was ready to be taken to the church.

It weighed more than nine hundred pounds, almost half a ton. The job of raising it into the belfry, hanging it securely and properly there, was a hard one.

Crowds of people gathered at the New Brick Church to hear the bell's first ringing. Paul was breathless with anxiety as to how it would sound. Rachel and the children stood beside him, sharing his concern.

The rope was pulled, the bell swung out, its clapper striking. Poor Paul! The ring was harsh and clangy. He stood there, horrified at the shrill, metallic sound. He thought his ears would burst if the sexton didn't stop ringing it. With the bell's clamor still shattering the air, Paul turned to leave and go back to the foundry. Friends in the crowd would stop him to say, "It has a good hardy ring, Revere." . . . "Folks can't claim now they were late for meeting because we don't have a bell!" . . . or, "England won't be sending bells to Boston any more." But words couldn't soften his bitter disappointment.

Rachel, her heart as heavy as his, called the children and took them home.

That night when she and Paul were alone in front of the fire, she said gently, "The bell rings clearly and loudly, Paul. Most people ask no more of a bell."

"It makes a fine clangy noise, all right!" Paul exclaimed. It's good for fire alarms—but that's all."

"Well, that's a noble use for a bell," Rachel answered. "Besides, your first batch of gunpowder didn't work; did it? Your early silver wasn't as perfect as the pieces you make today. You must look upon this bell as an experiment."

Paul sat there a moment, watching the fire, his eyes thoughtful. Then he said, "Yes, of course you are right. And I shall make more bells. But not until I've tried to find out why this one was a failure."

For the next few months many people probably thought Paul had gone crazy. He did practically nothing, but climb in and out of belfries. Up and down New England he went, listening for the sound of a sweet-toned bell. Whenever he heard one that pleased his ears, straight to the belfry he went.

Many a time he had a difficult climb to reach the bells. Some of the towers were rickety and unsafe. Most of them were dark and thick with dirt, hung with bats and spiders. But Paul climbed them all.

High in the belfry he would perch, measuring the bell, jotting down its various dimensions. He would tap it lightly and listen closely so that, by its very sound, he might be able to tell what metals it contained. He noticed carefully how the bell was hung, how the clapper was balanced in it.

Rachel saw him come home night after night, tired and grimy, his clothes often torn. But from the bells he was learning the things he needed to know. So, in spite of the weariness and dirt, he felt triumphant.

One day he announced triumphantly to Rachel, "I know now why the tone of my bell is so flat. I could have improved it by cutting off some of the bottom."

He spread out sheets of paper covered with small figures. "These figures tell me so—they are the measurements of bells. Oh, I see it now! The pitch, or key,

Paul studies bells in New England belfries

of the bell depends on the width of its diameter at the base. If it is flat, by cutting some off the bottom of the bell, I would make the diameter smaller. If a bell is sharp, the metal is cut off the inside of the bell, down near the bottom, making the diameter wider."

In the belfries Paul saw bells scarred by chisels in this tuning process. All these marks he carefully examined and recorded, for he must let nothing escape him.

His sensitive ears told him, too, that the beauty of a bell also depended on the metals that go into its making.

"Tin is the secret," he confided to Rachel. "People think silver added to the alloy improves the tone of a bell. But it doesn't. Copper and tin—that's the magic combination.

"Not too much tin, though. It will make it too brittle. I saw a beautiful bell, cracked and useless, because its maker was overanxious for tone and used more tin than it could stand."

So, by getting acquainted with bells, he learned the secrets. He examined big bells and little bells, new bells and old ones; cracked bells told him their weaknesses, poor bells their faults, beautiful bells their virtues.

At last Paul decided he was ready to try again. He wondered if people would risk giving him an order. For his first bell, while it still hung in the New Brick's belfry, was, as Paul said, good only for alarms. It was never rung except in case of fire. And a neighboring church graciously allowed the New Brick's sexton to come over and ring its sweet-toned bell for other purposes.

However, Paul boldly announced that again he was in the bell-casting business. Much to his delight, orders came in at once.

He set about casting these bells with a singing heart, for he knew what he was doing. As each bell was finished, Paul would move it from the foundry to the big yard behind his home. There he would tap it gently and listen to its sound. Carefully it would be pared down, the diameter widened or narrowed, according to its need, until it was perfect.

Rachel could look out the kitchen window and see Paul testing the bells. The yard was always crowded with schoolboys, watching and curious.

As year followed year, more and more bells were cast, for the fame of Paul's work spread far and near. Schools and churches and village meetinghouses all over New England wanted a beautiful Revere bell. From as far west as Kentucky, as far south as Georgia, came orders for them. Sailing ships bought them, and carried their music to distant ports. Plantation owners in Cuba, cathedrals in Porto Rico sent to Boston to buy bells from Paul Revere.

But even while Paul enjoyed this fresh success, his mind was busy with another scheme.

CHAPTER SIXTEEN

Paul Crowns a Rich Career

A SHIP sailed into Boston harbor one morning loaded with copper junk, consigned to Paul Revere. To the sailors, the copper was just ballast that had steadied the ship through rough seas. To Paul it was the material with which he would start a new experiment, the boldest and most ambitious task of all.

When Paul succeeded with the bells, Rachel had secretly hoped he would take things more easily, and enjoy a little leisure. He had worked hard for many years, and they had both earned a rest.

The older children were grown up and gone from home. Young Paul was in business for himself, Deborah married and with a family of her own. Joseph Warren, the child born while Paul was away at war, was now in his teens, and big enough to help at the foundry. John, their youngest and their last, had started school. There would be no more babies at the Revere house. Paul's responsibilities were lessening.

The foundry brought in a tidy income, and there were no financial worries. The house on Charter Street was spacious and comfortable, its gardens bright with flowers, lush with fruit in summer, its rooms warm with firelight and friendliness in winter, the kitchen always fragrant with good things cooking.

But, with the bell casting firmly established, Paul began working, harder than ever, on experiments with copper. America then had to import from England the copper spikes and bolts and staples needed in building, and the sheets of copper so important for sheathing the nation's ships. Paul, still intensely eager to see new industries established in his country, was determined to discover the processes for successfully working copper.

When, after tedious experiments, he learned how to draw the copper into spikes, Paul was proud. But he was still dissatisfied.

"I want to be able to roll copper," he said stubbornly. "Our new State House will soon be finished, ready for its copper-covered dome. The government is building frigates that need copper-covered hulls. We shouldn't be buying copper sheets from England for these!"

Since mines had not yet been opened up in this country, Paul set about his experiments with scrap copper, the junk brought as ballast in the ship's hold.

Paul knew a great deal about the behavior of metals, for he had worked with them since he was a young boy. Even so, the years that followed were filled with hard work at wearing experiments, failures and disappointments—and, finally, success.

Once more Rachel saw every cent they had plunged into a new and untried business. "It will take every farthing I can scrape together," Paul admitted. "The machinery needed must be brought from England. And I'll need a large tract of land, outside the city, and buildings———"

His plans soared, and Rachel was speechless at his daring. Suppose it failed? Paul was no longer a young man. Yet here he was, launching a new business, going into debt for it, staking everything on it just as fearlessly as he might have at twenty.

Paul remembered the site of the old powder mill at Canton where many years before he had experimented with gunpowder. "I'll buy that land," he planned, "put up my buildings there."

But the expenses of his project were even greater than he figured. Though he had pooled all the money he could lay his hands on, there wasn't nearly enough.

"I need ten thousand dollars," he said. "I'll have to borrow it."

"Ten thousand!" Rachel gasped. "Why, Paul, that's a fortune!"

"Yes, I know. But I must have it."

"Where could you ever borrow an amount that large?"

"I'm going to Washington, Rachel, to ask the government for it. I've worked for many years trying to build this new industry, trying to make our country independent of England in yet another way. Surely the government should be willing to help me."

This was the longest journey Paul had ever made. But when he came back to Boston, he came triumphant. The government had agreed to lend him the ten thousand dollars, and to take copper sheeting in payment for the debt.

So the buildings went up at Canton, the machinery was installed, and the manufacture of rolled copper begun. The first shining sheets that came from the plant were used for covering the dome of the State House. Seven years earlier Paul had been chosen to lay the cornerstone of the building. Now his copper provided the finishing touch, completing it.

The plant at Canton boomed. Newspapers printed stories about it, for it was the only place in America where copper sheeting could be made. Orders crowded in until Paul's chief worry was that of getting enough copper to roll! The government was speedily paid back, and again there was enough money so Paul and Rachel had no worries. These were proud days for both of them.

Perhaps on no day were they prouder than the sunny June afternoon in 1803, when they stood down at the harbor and watched the frigate *Constitution* floated, her hull newly sheathed with burnished copper made by Paul.

As the ship put out into the harbor, the voices of sailors and carpenters and calkers rose in cheers for the first American ship to be coppered with metal made at home.

Paul was the hero of the occasion, as the white sails filled and the ship swept across the blue water. Paul had made the metal parts that gave her strength and power. Her bolts and pumps and spikes, every tiny dovetail and staple, her copper armor, she owed to Paul. Even her bell, that showered silvery notes back to those who watched her disappear, had been cast by him.

Soon ships armored with Paul's copper and strengthened with copper fastenings, were sailing from Boston to foreign ports all over the world. Paul liked to think of these ships he had helped build, riding safely through tropical storms, buffeting the gales of the northern seas, unloading their American cargoes on strange shores.

Wherever he went now, there were signs of his handiwork. The bell ringing sweetly from a near-by tower was one of his making. He could see the State House dome on Beacon Hill shining with his copper. At church the silver communion service that softly reflected the morning light had come from his hands. At the homes of friends, he was served from platters

Paul still has plans for tomorrow

of his own design. The things he had made would live long after he was gone, for he had made them well.

In Canton, within sight of his plant, he built a summer home and surrounded it with gardens for Rachel. There Rachel worked among the flowers, while Paul was busy at the foundry. And there the children and grandchildren gathered on summer evenings and listened to Paul tell stories of the past and make prophecies for the future.

One bright morning when Paul was starting for the plant, Rachel said to him, "Paul, why don't you stop working? You're an old man. You're in your seventies. Why don't you retire?"

A smile spread slowly over his face, and his dark eyes twinkled. He answered as if he had never heard her, "I want to get to the plant early today," he said, "We're rolling special-sized copper sheets for a fellow in New York some folks think crazy. His name is Robert Fulton. Needs the copper to make boilers for a contraption he calls a steamboat."

Rachel sighed and kissed him, and watched him down the path. The sun shone on his thin white hair, but his step was still brisk, his head ever full of plans for tomorrow.